A PURPOSE DRIVEN LEADERSHIP COURSE

How to Be a Purpose Driven

CHURCH

LEARNER'S GUIDE

RICK WARREN

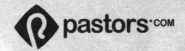

Purpose Driven Leadership Course: Learners Guide, Edition 1.0

Published by Pastors.com
30021 Comercio
Rancho Santa Margarita, CA 92688
www.saddlebackresources.com

Cover design   Riley Hall
Interior design   Betty Hopkins

ISBN: 978-1-4228-0243-4

Printed and bound in the United States of America.

CONTENTS

Course Goals

1. To Encourage Our Spirits

Encourage each other and build each other up.

1 Thessalonians 5:11a (NLT)

Let us not get tired of doing what is right, for after a while we will reap a harvest of blessing if we don't get discouraged and give up.

Galatians 6:9 (TLB)

2. To Stretch Our Minds

Do yourself a favor and learn all you can; then remember what you learn and you will prosper.

Proverbs 19:8 (TEV)

How can you teach others when you refuse to learn?

Romans 2:21a (CEV)

The intelligent man is always open to new ideas. In fact, he looks for them.

Proverbs 18:15 (TLB)

3. To Sharpen Our Skills

If the ax is dull and its edge is unsharpened, more strength is needed, but skill will bring success.

Ecclesiastes 10:10 (NIV)

4. To Strengthen Our Church

Under [Christ's] direction, the whole body is fitted together perfectly. As each part does its own special work, it helps the other parts grow, so that the whole body is healthy and growing and full of love.

Ephesians 4:16 (NLT)

5. To Focus Our Vision

But these things I plan won't happen right away. Slowly, steadily, surely, the time approaches when the vision will be fulfilled. If it seems slow, do not despair, for these things will surely come to pass. Just be patient! They will not be overdue a single day!

Habakkuk 2:3 (TLB)

God is never late.

Building a Purpose Driven Church

Establishing a Foundation for Growth

The Right Question: What Is _Keeping_
My Church from Growing?

Growth Comes from _health_

Health Comes from _balance_

→ all living. Things grow.
Healthy things grow.
Natural for growth. Unnatural not to grow

SESSION 1 ~ BUILDING A PURPOSE DRIVEN CHURCH

9 Body systems in balance ⇒ growth.

Every Church Is Directed By Some Force

. . . By Tradition — *we've always/never done it that way before*

. . . By Personalities — *ministry collapses when that person fails/dies/moves on*

. . . By Finances — *"how much will it cost?"*

. . . By Buildings —

. . . By Programs —

. . . By Events — *wear people out.*

. . . By the Unchurched —

A Biblical Alternative: Become a _____*Purpose*_____ Driven Church!

> *Many are the plans in a man's heart, but it is the Lord's* *purpose* *that prevails.*
>
> Proverbs 19:21 (NIV)

Jesus' church, Jesus builds it

> *"I will build my church; and the gates of hell shall not prevail against it!"*
>
> Matthew 16:18 (KJV)

Growing churches have a clear picture of its identity & purpose.

Defining Our Church's Purposes

Why Is It Important?

1. It Builds ___moral___

[handwritten: Common purpose keeps moral high]

> *Let there be real harmony so that there won't be splits in the church . . . Be of one mind, united in thought and purpose.*
>
> **1 Corinthians 1:10 (TLB)**

> *Where there is no vision, the people perish.*
>
> **Proverbs 29:18a (KJV)**

[handwritten: Programs don't motivate. Purpose motivates.]

2. It Reduces ___frustration___

[handwritten left margin: Define role before you set goals.]

> *You, Lord, give perfect peace to those who keep their purpose firm . . .*
>
> **Isaiah 26:3 (GNB)**

> *The double-minded man can never keep a steady course.*
>
> **James 1:8 (NEB)**

> *I have labored to no purpose; I have spent my strength in vain and for nothing.*
>
> **Isaiah 49:4 (NIV)**

[handwritten: Purpose statement tells what we do and what we don't do.]

7

3. *It Allows* _Concentration_

> *I am bringing all my energies to bear on <u>this one</u> <u>thing</u>: forgetting the past and looking forward to what lies ahead.*
>
> **Philippians 3:13** (TLB)

Efficiency: "Doing things right"

Effectiveness: "Doing the right things"

4. *It Attracts* _Cooperation_

> *"Tell us how to proceed in setting things straight, and we will fully <u>cooperate</u>."*
>
> **Ezra 10:4b** (TLB)

> <u>*You have helped me in the work of the gospel*</u> *. . .*
>
> **Philippians 1:5** (GNB)

> *If your goals are good, you will be respected.*
>
> **Proverbs 11:27** (GNB)

5. *It Assists* _Examination_

> *Examine yourselves to see whether you are in the faith; test yourselves.*
>
> **2 Corinthians 13:5** (NIV)

SESSION 1 ~ BUILDING A PURPOSE DRIVEN CHURCH

What Is the Biblical Foundation for the Purposes of the Church?

THE GREAT COMMANDMENT

"LOVE THE LORD YOUR GOD with all your heart . . . soul . . . and mind. This is the first and greatest commandment. And the second is like it: LOVE YOUR NEIGHBOR as yourself. All the Law and the Prophets hang on these two commandments."

Matthew 22:37–40 (NIV)

THE GREAT COMMISSION

"GO AND MAKE DISCIPLES of all nations, BAPTIZING THEM in the name of the Father and of the Son and of the Holy Spirit, and TEACHING THEM TO [DO] everything I have commanded you."

Matthew 28:19–20 (NIV)

Five Purposes for the Church

1. *"Love God with all your heart"*   _worship_

2. *"Love your neighbor as yourself"*   _ministry_

3. *"Go . . . make disciples"*   _evangelism_

4. *"Baptize them"*   _fellowship_

5. *"Teach them to DO"*   _discipleship_

Jesus' ministry modeled these 5 purposes: John 17:1–26 (NIV)

Verse 4   **"I have brought you glory on earth." (WORSHIP)**

Verse 6   **"I revealed you to those whom you gave me out of the world." (EVANGELISM)**

Verse 8   **"I gave them the words you gave me." (DISCIPLESHIP)**

Verse 12   **"While I was with them, I protected them and kept them safe." (FELLOWSHIP)**

Verse 18   **"As you sent me into the world, I have sent them into the world." (MINISTRY)**

SESSION 1 ~ BUILDING A PURPOSE DRIVEN CHURCH

The first church fulfilled these 5 purposes: Acts 2:41–47 (NIV)

> *Those who accepted his message were baptized . . . They devoted themselves to the apostles' teaching (DISCIPLESHIP) and to the fellowship (FELLOWSHIP), to the breaking of bread and to prayer . . . All the believers were together . . . they gave to anyone as he had need (MINISTRY) . . . Every day they continued to meet together in the temple courts. They broke bread in their homes and ate together with glad and sincere hearts, praising God (WORSHIP) . . . And the Lord added to their number daily those who were being saved (EVANGELISM).*

Paul explained these 5 purposes: Ephesians 4:11–16 (NIV)

> [God] *gave some to be apostles, some to be prophets, some to be evangelists, and some to be pastors and teachers, to prepare God's people for works of* [ministry], *so that the body of Christ may be built up until we all reach unity in the faith and in the knowledge of the Son of God and become mature, attaining to the whole measure of the fullness of Christ . . . From him the whole body, joined and held together by every supporting ligament, grows and builds itself up in love, as each part does its work.*

So to Summarize—The Church Exists to . . .

1. CELEBRATE GOD'S _Presence_ **(WORSHIP)**

"Exalt our Master"

O magnify the Lord with me, and let us exalt his name together.

Psalm 34:3 (NRSV)

I was glad when they said to me, "Let us go to the Lord's house."

Psalm 122:1 (GNB)

2. COMMUNICATE GOD'S _Word_ **(EVANGELISM)**

"Evangelize our mission field"

The most important thing is that I complete my mission, the work the Lord Jesus gave me to do—to tell people the Good News about God's grace.

Acts 20:24 (NCV)

"You will be my witnesses . . ."

Acts 1:8b (NIV)

SESSION 1 ~ BUILDING A PURPOSE DRIVEN CHURCH

3. INCORPORATE GOD'S _____*family*_____ (FELLOWSHIP)

"Encourage our members"

> *You are members of God's very own family . . . and you belong in God's household with every other Christian.*
>
> Ephesians 2:19 (TLB)

4. EDUCATE GOD'S _____*people*_____ (DISCIPLESHIP)

"Educate for maturity"

> *Building up the Church, the body of Christ, to a position of strength and maturity; until . . . all become full-grown in the Lord.*
>
> Ephesians 4:12b–13 (TLB)

5. DEMONSTRATE GOD'S _____*love*_____ (MINISTRY)

"Equip for ministry"

> *To equip [God's people] for the work of ministry.*
>
> Ephesians 4:12a (ESV)

13

*Define first,
then →* ***Communicating Our Purposes***

It's not enough to simply define our purposes!

The number one task of leadership is to continually clarify and communicate the purpose of the organization.

Five Ways to Communicate Vision and Purpose

1. Slogans

2. Symbols *communicate values*

3. Scriptures

4. Stories

5. Specifics *Here's how we do ___!*

SESSION 1 ~ BUILDING A PURPOSE DRIVEN CHURCH

Adopt a Purpose Driven Slogan and
Statement for Our Congregation

PURPOSE DRIVEN *S*LOGAN

A GREAT COMMITMENT

TO THE GREAT COMMANDMENT

AND THE GREAT COMMISSION

WILL GROW A GREAT CHURCH!

PURPOSE DRIVEN PURPOSE *S*TATEMENT

To bring people to Jesus and membership in his family, develop them to Christ-like maturity, and equip them for their ministry in the church and their life mission in the world, in order to magnify God's name.

Bring them in . . . Build them up
Teach them how . . . Send them out!

LEARNER'S GUIDE

Here are some ways purpose driven churches communicate their purposes to their congregations:

- Every Membership Class 101
- Annual message
- Monthly emphasis
- Print them in the bulletin
- Articles and brochures
- Monthly Pastor's coffee
- Sermons!

Explaining the Church's Purposes

Purposes	Tasks	Acts 2:42–47	Objectives	Targets	Life Components	Basic Human Needs	The Church Provides	Emotional Benefits
Outreach	Evangelize	"Added to their number daily those who were being saved."	Mission	Community	My **Witness**	**Purpose** to Live For	A **Focus** for Living	Significance
Worship	Exalt	"They devoted themselves to . . . breaking of bread and prayers . . . praising God."	Magnify	Crowd	My **Worship**	**Power** to Live On	A **Force** for Living	Stimulation
Fellowship	Encourage	"Devoted to the followship . . . all the believers were together . . . they ate together."	Membership	Congregation	My **Relationships**	**People** to Live With	A **Family** for Living	Support
Discipleship	Edify	"They devoted themselves to the apostles' teaching."	Maturity	Committed	My **Walk**	**Principles** to Live By	A **Foundation** for Living	Stability
Service	Equip	"They gave to anyone as he had need."	Ministry	Core	My **Work**	**Profession** to Live Out	A **Function** for Living	Self-expression

SESSION 1 ~ BUILDING A PURPOSE DRIVEN CHURCH

Let's pause here and spend a few minutes talking with each other. Which of these purposes are you most passionate about?

_____

_____

_____

_____

_____

_____

_____

_____

_____

_____

_____

_____

_____

_____

_____

_____

_____

_____

Applying Our Purposes

**It's not enough to just define
and communicate our purposes.**

**We must apply the purposes to every
area of our church's life.**

The Key to Applying the Purposes Is _____

We must have a system and structure in place to keep the five purposes in
balance in our church.

SESSION 1 ~ BUILDING A PURPOSE DRIVEN CHURCH

Most Churches Tend to Focus on Only One Purpose								
Paradigms	**Primary Focuses**	**Pastor's Roles**	**People's Roles**	**Targets**	**Key Terms**	**Central Values**	**Tools Used**	**Source of Legitimacy**
Soul Winning church	Evangelism	Evangelist	Witnesses	Community	Save	Decisions for Christ	Visitation and Altar Call	Number Baptized
Experiencing God church	Worship	Worship Leader	Worshipers	Crowd	Feel	Personal Experience	Music and Prayer	"The Spirit"
The Family Reunion church	Fellowship	Chaplain	Family Members	Congregation	Belong	Loyalty and Tradition	Fellowship Hall and Potluck	Our Heritage
Bible Classroom church	Edification	Instructor	Students	Committed	Know	Bible Knowledge	Notebooks and Overheads	Verse-by-Verse Teaching
Social Conscience church	Ministry	Reformer	Activists	Core	Care	Justice and Mercy	Petitions and Placards	Number of Needs Met
The Purpose Driven Church Philosophy Insures Balance								
Purpose Driven church	**Balance All Five**	**Equipper**	**Ministers**	**All Five**	**Be and Do**	**Christ-like Character**	**Life Development Process**	**Changed Lives**

**Only a purpose driven strategy
and structure can maintain balance.**

How to Balance the Five Purposes

Begin to see six target groups that we minister to.

1. Identify Our Targets On Purpose

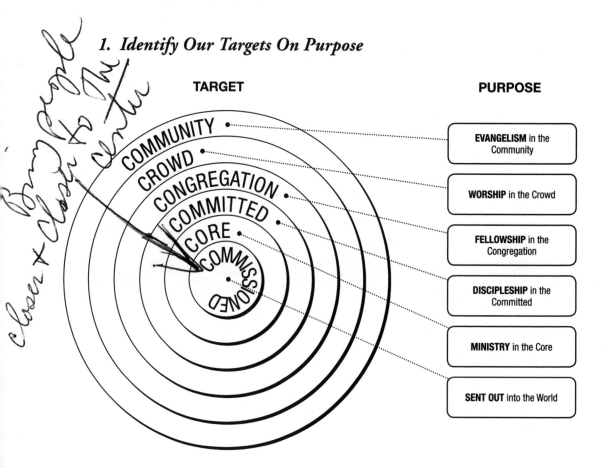

TARGET

PURPOSE

Bring people Closer + Closer to The Center

COMMUNITY

CROWD

CONGREGATION

COMMITTED

CORE

COMMISSIONED

EVANGELISM in the Community	
WORSHIP in the Crowd	
FELLOWSHIP in the Congregation	
DISCIPLESHIP in the Committed	
MINISTRY in the Core	
SENT OUT into the World	

SESSION 1 ~ BUILDING A PURPOSE DRIVEN CHURCH

GROUPS		HOW BIG ARE OUR CIRCLES?
COMMUNITY	**People who attend occasionally**	_____
CROWD	**Average attendance each week at worship**	
CONGREGATION	**Completed Membership Class 101** **Committed to the Membership Covenant,** **baptized, joined our fellowship.**	_____
COMMITTED	**Completed Maturity Class 201** **Committed to the Maturity Covenant to tithe,** **attend a small group, and have a quiet time.**	_____
CORE	**Completed Discovering My Ministry Class 301** **Committed to the Ministry Covenant,** **and are serving in Ministry**	_____
COMMISSIONED	**Completed Missions Class 401** **Committed to the Mission Covenant,** **and participate in The PEACE Plan**	_____

LEARNER'S GUIDE

2. *Educate Our People On Purpose*

Build our Christian Education program around the five purposes.

THE PURPOSE DRIVEN CLASS SYSTEM

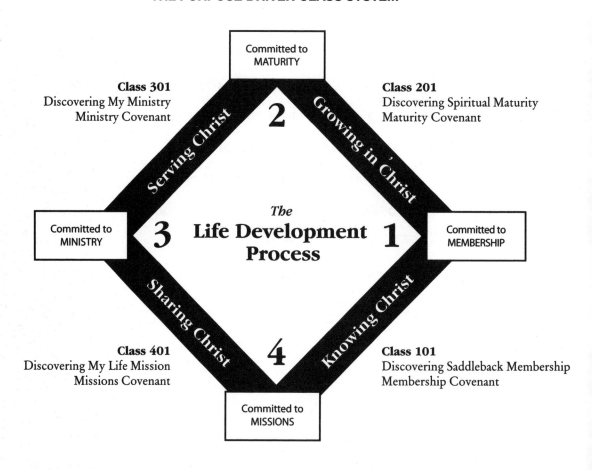

SESSION 1 ~ BUILDING A PURPOSE DRIVEN CHURCH

The Priorities of a Purpose Driven Church

Priority #1: God's Purposes

In a Purpose Driven church, God's purposes take priority over everything else.

Priority #2: People

People are here to fulfill the eternal purposes of God.

Priority #3: Programs

Programs are simply tools to help people fulfill the purposes.

Priority #4: Property

Property is simply a place to conduct programs to help people fulfill the purposes.

Building a Purpose Driven Church: Personal & Church Exercise

1. Which purpose do you feel most passionate about?

2. How could you better balance God's purposes in your own life?

3. Which of the five New Testament purposes has our church tended to emphasize the most? Which of the five purposes has our church tended to emphasize least?

4. What ideas do the symbols of the concentric circles and the diamond give you about how we could balance the five purposes in our church?

Session 2

Reaching Our Community

Learning to Fish for Souls Like Jesus

6 principles of Evangelism

"Come along with me and I will show you how to fish for the souls of men."

Matthew 4:19 (TLB)

Jesus' Strategy of Fishing for People

See Matthew 10 and Luke 10.

1. Know What You Are *fishing for*

You must identify who you are trying to reach.

Jesus had a clear evangelistic target:

"I was sent only to the lost sheep of Israel." **Matthew 15:24 (NIV)**

Not to be exclusive but to be effective

Paul had a clear evangelistic target:

I had been entrusted with the task of preaching the gospel to the Gentiles, just as Peter had been to the Jews. **Galatians 2:7 (NIV)**

Jesus gave the disciples a clear evangelistic target:

"Don't go among the Gentiles or enter any town of the Samaritans. Go rather to the lost sheep of Israel." **Matthew 10:5–6 (NIV)**

SESSION 2 ~ REACHING OUR COMMUNITY

How to Define Our Target

1. *Define Our Target Geographically*

    ASK: How many people live in this area?

2. *Define Our Target Demographically*

    ASK: What kind of people live in this area?

3. *Define Our Target Culturally*

    ASK: What are their values, interests and fears?

    BEST SOURCE: Personal survey

LEARNER'S GUIDE

 Define Our Target Spiritually

ASK: What do they already know about the gospel?

Determine their religious background.

FACT: All unchurched people are not alike!

Now Personalize Our Target!

Develop a profile of our typical unchurched resident.

SESSION 2 ~ REACHING OUR COMMUNITY

"Saddleback Sam" — Our Target
The Likely Mr. South Orange County, California

He is well educated.

He likes contemporary music.

He likes his job.

He thinks he is enjoying life more than he did five years ago.

He likes where he lives.

He is self-satisfied, even smug, about his station in life.

Health and fitness are high priorities for him and his family.

He prefers the casual and informal over the formal.

He'd rather be in a large group than a small one.

He is overextended in both time and money.

He is skeptical of "organized" religion.

Who is the target of our church?

You've got to know who your target is. The more defined your target is the easier it is to reach him.

2. Learn to *think like a fish*

Jesus knew what they were thinking . . .
> Matthew 9:4; 12:25; Mark 2:8; Luke 5:22; 9:47; 11:17

"I send you out as sheep in the midst of wolves.
Therefore, be wise as serpents and harmless as doves."
> Matthew 10:16 (NKJV)

Be wise in the way you act toward those who are
not believers . . .
> Colossians 4:5 (GNB)

THE PROBLEM: The longer I am a believer, *the less*
I think like an unbeliever.

"Resistance" Is Often Just Poor Communication

Think like your target if you want to reach your target

Resistance to the Gospel is just being on a different wave length.

30

SESSION 2 ~ REACHING OUR COMMUNITY

How to Discover the "Mind-set" of Unbelievers: <u>Ask Them</u>

**If you don't ask the right questions,
you won't get the right answers.**

**If you don't get the right answers,
you won't develop the right strategy.**

**If you don't develop the right strategy,
you won't get the right results.**

How Saddleback Began: A "Personal Opinion Poll"

FIVE QUESTIONS TO ASK

1. **ARE YOU CURRENTLY ACTIVE IN A LOCAL CHURCH?**

2. **WHAT DO YOU FEEL IS THE GREATEST NEED IN THIS AREA?**

LEARNER'S GUIDE

3. **WHY DO YOU THINK MOST PEOPLE DON'T ATTEND CHURCH?**

4. **IF YOU WERE LOOKING FOR A CHURCH, WHAT KIND OF THINGS WOULD YOU LOOK FOR?**

5. **WHAT ADVICE WOULD YOU GIVE ME? HOW CAN I HELP YOU?**

The Four Greatest Complaints In the Saddleback Valley

1. **SERMONS ARE BORING AND IRRELEVANT**

SESSION 2 ~ REACHING OUR COMMUNITY

2. MEMBERS ARE UNFRIENDLY TO VISITORS

3. TOO MUCH EMPHASIS ON MONEY

4. POOR CHILDCARE

OUR CONCLUSION: Most unchurched people are not atheists.

They're just turned off and too busy!

Saddleback's First Letter to the Commmunity

March 20, 1980

Hi Neighbor!

AT LAST!
A NEW CHURCH FOR THOSE WHO HAVE
GIVEN UP ON TRADITIONAL CHURCH SERVICES!

Let's face it . . . many people aren't active in church these days.

WHY?

Too often:
- *the sermons are boring and don't relate to daily living*
- *many churches seem more interested in your wallet than in you*
- *members are unfriendly to visitors*
- *you wonder about the quality of the nursery care for your little ones*

Do you think attending church should be enjoyable?

WELL, WE'VE GOT GOOD NEWS FOR YOU!

SADDLEBACK VALLEY COMMUNITY CHURCH is a new church designed to meet your needs in the 1980's. We're a group of friendly, happy people who have discovered the joy of the Christian lifestyle.

At Saddleback Valley Community Church you:
- *meet new friends and get to know your neighbors*
- *enjoy exciting music with a contemporary flavor*
- *hear positive, practical messages which uplift you each week*
- *trust your children to the care of dedicated nursery workers*

WHY NOT GET A LIFT INSTEAD OF A LETDOWN THIS SUNDAY?

I invite you to be my special guest at our first public celebration service EASTER SUNDAY, April 6, at 11:00 a.m. We are currently meeting in the Laguna Hills High School Theater. If you don't have a church home, give us a try! DISCOVER THE DIFFERENCE!

Sincerely,

Rick Warren, Pastor

P.S. If you don't own a Bible, we'd like to give you a free New Testament. Just return the enclosed reply card.

SESSION 2 ~ REACHING OUR COMMUNITY

3. Go _____

Let our target determine our approach.

"When you enter a town and are welcomed, eat what is set before you."

Luke 10:8 (NIV)

PAUL'S EVANGELISM STRATEGY

To the Jews I became like a Jew, to win the Jews . . . In the same way, when working with Gentiles, I live like a Gentile . . . in order to win the Gentiles. I become all things to all people, that I may save some of them by whatever means are possible.

1 Corinthians 9:20–22 (NIV/GNB)

Whatever a person is like, I try to find common ground with him so that he will let me tell him about Christ and let Christ save him.

1 Corinthians 9:22 (TLB)

LEARNER'S GUIDE

JESUS' STANDARD APPROACH: _____

Purpose Driven Evangelism Strategy

• THE NEEDS OF UNBELIEVERS

DETERMINE OUR _____

> *Jesus said, "It is not the healthy who need a doctor, but the sick. I have not come to call the righteous, but sinners."*
>
> Mark 2:17 (NIV)

> *Jesus said, "What do you want me to do for you?"*
> Matthew 20:32; Mark 10:51; Luke 18:41

**Anyone can be won to Christ
if you discover the key to his heart.**

THE KEY: FELT NEEDS

**Before you can share the Good News, you must
first capture their attention.**

SESSION 2 ~ REACHING OUR COMMUNITY

THE SECRET OF SUCCESS: MEETING NEEDS

**Our church will never grow
beyond our capacity to meet needs.**

THE FELT NEEDS OF THE UNCHURCHED ARE PRIMARILY:

_____ **AND** _____

- **THE MIND-SET OF UNBELIEVERS**

  DETERMINES OUR _____

  "Be wise as serpents and harmless as doves!"
  Matthew 10:16 (NKJV)

  *"The people of this world are more shrewd in dealing
  with their own kind than are the people of the light."*
  Luke 16:8 (NIV)

- **THE CULTURE OF UNBELIEVERS**

  DETERMINES OUR _____

KEY QUESTION: WHO ARE WE TRYING TO IMPRESS

4. Find the Fish That Are _____

Focus on the most receptive audience in the area.

> *"If a home or town refuses to welcome you or listen to you, leave that place and shake its dust off your feet."*
>
> **Matthew 10:14** (NCV)

> *Jesus told him, "You are not far from the Kingdom of God."*
>
> **Mark 12:34** (TEV)

- Growing churches focus on reaching receptive people
- Non-growing churches focus on re-enlisting inactive people

Who are the most receptive people?

- Those _____
- Those _____

5. Use _____

Offer people choices.

The more hooks you use, _____

I become all things to all people so that I may save some of them by whatever means are possible.

1 Corinthians 9:22 (GNB)

We live in a world full of choices!

SATURATION EVANGELISM

Using every available means

to reach every available person

at every available time.

Why We Usually Fish with Only One Hook

The wrong question: How much will it _____?

The right question: Who will it _____?

Financing Evangelism In Our Church

1. MONEY SPENT ON EVANGELISM IS NEVER AN "EXPENSE,"

IT IS _____ .

2. CHURCHES NEVER REALLY HAVE "MONEY PROBLEMS,"

THEY HAVE _____ .

Hudson Taylor said:
"God's work done God's way will not lack

_____."

Exercise

Personal Exercise

Write down the names of 5 people you are praying will come to know Jesus.

_____

_____

_____

_____

Church Exercise

How to Get Started In Targeting Our Own Community

PROBE: LEARN ALL WE CAN ABOUT OUR AREA

What do we know already?

_____

_____

How can we learn more?

_____

_____

LEARNER'S GUIDE

PARTITION: DIVIDE OUR AREA INTO SEGMENTS

What are the major segments of our community?

_____

_____

_____

_____

_____

PRIORITIZE: CHOOSE WHICH GROUP TO GO AFTER FIRST

Who has God called us to reach?

_____

_____

_____

_____

Does this match who we are?

_____

_____

_____

_____

_____

SESSION 2 ~ REACHING OUR COMMUNITY

POSITION: DEVELOP A CLEAR IMAGE OF THE TYPE OF CHURCH WE WANT TO BE BASED ON WHO WE WANT TO ATTRACT!

If we are to reach the group God is calling us to reach:

... what strengths do we already have?

_____

_____

_____

_____

_____

... what strengths do we need to develop?

_____

_____

_____

_____

... what changes will we need to consider?

_____

_____

_____

_____

Session 3

Attracting a Crowd to Worship

How to Design a Worship Service That Is a Witness to Unbelievers

Facts About Crowds

Jesus' ministry attracted enormous crowds.

Enormous crowds followed him wherever he went ...
Matthew 4:25 (TLB)

SESSION 3 ~ ATTRACTING A CROWD TO WORSHIP

When he saw the crowds, he had compassion on them, because they were harassed and helpless, like sheep without a shepherd.

                                                            Matthew 9:36 (NIV)

The large crowd listened to him with delight.

                                                            Mark 12:37 (NIV)

God wants his house FULL!

"Go out into the highways and hedges, and compel them to come in, that my house may be filled."

                                                            Luke 14:23 (KJV)

No church grows without visitors.

A crowd is not a church . . .

BUT it can become a church—if you have a strategy.

Twelve Convictions About Worship

1. Only believers can truly worship God.

   "God is spirit, and his worshipers must worship in spirit and in truth."

   John 4:24 (NIV)

   Worship is expressing our love to God for who he is, what he's said, and what he's doing.

2. You don't need a building to worship God!

   The God who made the world and everything in it is the Lord of heaven and earth and does not live in temples built by hands.

   Acts 17:24 (NIV)

3. There is no correct "style" of worship.

   "God is spirit, and his worshipers must worship in spirit and in truth."

   John 4:24 (NIV)

4. Unbelievers CAN watch believers worship.

SESSION 3 ~ ATTRACTING A CROWD TO WORSHIP

5. Worship is a powerful witness to unbelievers if God's presence is felt and the message is understandable.

   . . . a crowd came together.

   polite

   Acts 2:6 (NIV)

6. God expects us to be sensitive to the fears, hang-ups, and needs of unbelievers when they are present in our worship services.

   So if the whole church comes together and everyone speaks in tongues, and some who do not understand or some unbelievers come in, will they not say that you are out of your mind?

   1 Corinthians 14:23 (NIV)

   Do not cause anyone to stumble, whether Jews, Greeks or the church of God.

   1 Corinthians 10:32 (NIV)

   Be tactful with those who are not Christians and be sure you make the best use of your time with them.

   Colossians 4:5 (JB)

7. A worship service does not have to be shallow to be evangelistic.

**The message doesn't have
to be compromised—just understandable!**

*If I don't understand the language, it's not going to do
me much good.*

1 Corinthians 14:11 (MSG)

8. The needs of believers and unbelievers often overlap—they are very different in some areas but are very similar in many areas.

9. It is best to specialize services according to their purpose.

**If we send mixed signals,
we get mixed results!**

For greatest evangelistic impact:

Weekend services focus on evangelism

Small Group/Midweek studies focus on edification

10. A service geared toward seekers is meant to supplement personal evangelism, not replace it.

11. There is no standard way to design an evangelistic worship service.

What really attracts large numbers of unchurched to a church is:

Changed lives

12. It takes unselfish, mature believers to offer an evangelistic worship service.

> *We haven't used our rights. Instead, we would put up with anything in order not to hinder the Good News of Christ in any way.*
>
> 1 Corinthians 9:12 (GWT)

The tension between "service" and "serve-us"

> *"Your attitude must be like my own, for I, the Messiah, did not come to be served, but to serve . . . "*
>
> Matthew 20:28 (TLB)

Checklist for an Evangelistic Worship Service

☐ **DO WE MAKE IT AS EASY AS POSSIBLE TO ATTEND?**

- **Offer multiple services.**

- **Offer surplus parking.**

- **Offer children's classes at the same time as the service.**

- **Put a map on all advertisements.**

☐ **DO WE HAVE GOOD PACE AND FLOW IN OUR SERVICE?**

- **Look for ways to save time.**

- **Minimize transition times.**

- **Keep pastoral prayers short.**

☐ **DO WE FOCUS ON MAKING VISITORS FEEL WELCOME?**

First 12 minutes—visitors decide if they'll come back.

You never get a second chance to make a first impression.

A visitor's first emotion: _____!

Our job is to reduce it!

SESSION 3 ~ ATTRACTING A CROWD TO WORSHIP

- Reserve our best parking spots for visitors.

- Station greeters outside our building.

- Set up an information table (or two!).

- Place directional signs and maps everywhere.

- Have recorded music playing when people enter. It relaxes people.

- Allow visitors to remain anonymous in the service. (People love to be greeted personally but not publicly.)

- Encourage everyone to fill out a welcome card.

- Offer a warm, casual public welcome that relaxes people.

- Begin and end each service by having people greet each other.

- Make nametags available to everyone (smaller churches).

- Offer a refreshment table at each service.

☐ DO WE HAVE A GOOD ENVIRONMENT?

FACILITIES: Look at our facilities from the eyes of a visitor!

ASK: "What message is our building giving off?"

THE PROBLEM: We tend to overlook things after just four weeks.

Ways to Brighten Up Our Environment

- **LIGHTING:** Is it bright enough?

  God is light, and in him is no darkness at all.

                                                    1 John 1:5 (ESV)

- **TEMPERATURE:** too warm or too cold kills a service.

- **SOUND:** Buy the best you can afford.

- **SEATING ARRANGEMENTS:** Provide enough space between seats. Let people see each other's faces. Set up fewer chairs than you need.

- **DISTANCE FROM THE PULPIT TO SEATS:** The smaller the crowds, the closer the speaker needs to be to the people.

- **DECORATIONS:** The best and cheapest are plants.

- **NURSERIES:** Make sure they are clean and safe.

- **RESTROOMS:** Clean and odor-free!

☐ **DO WE HELP VISITORS UNDERSTAND THE WORSHIP SERVICE?**

- **Print a bulletin with an order of service.**

- **Minimize internal church announcements.**

- **Announce only the events that apply to everyone.**

- **Screen out "in-house" terminology.**

- **Avoid appeals for help.**

SESSION 3 ~ ATTRACTING A CROWD TO WORSHIP

- **Don't conduct internal church business during the evangelistic worship service**

- **Help Those Who Are Unfamiliar With the Bible.**

  - ⊖ **Use pew Bibles so they can find the text by page number!**

  - ⊖ **Select scripture readings appropriate for our target.**

  - ⊖ **Provide an outline with the verses printed out.**

- **Preach with Our Target and Purpose In Mind.**

- **Match Our Music to Those We Want to Reach.**

  - ⊖ **Music is the #1 factor in who our church will reach and who our church will never reach.**

- **Always expect people to respond!**

- **Use the registration card as a decision card.**

☐ **DO WE CONTINUALLY EVALUATE AND IMPROVE**

ASK: What can we do better next Sunday?

Three Tools You Can Use for Evaluation

- **Attendance registration card**

- **Visitor's first impression reply card**

- **Staff worship evaluation form**

My SADDLEBACK RESPONSE CARD

Date _____   Email Address _____   ☐ New Email Address

Your Age Group

PLEASE PRINT

☐ 18–23   ☐ 24–29   ☐ 30's
☐ 40's   ☐ 50's   ☐ 60's
☐ 70's   ☐ 80's

Mr./Mrs./Miss/Ms.   ☐ New Address

Name _____

(If A Student) Your Current School Grade:

Address _____

1 2 3 4 5 6 7 8 9 10 11 12 College

City _____ State _____ Zip _____

I am: ☐ Single   ☐ Married

Home Phone (____) _____

Names of children living at home and birthdates:

Work Phone (____) _____

_____

Is this your ... ☐ 1st time? ☐ 2nd time? ☐ 3rd time?

_____

I am: ☐ Attender ☐ Member

_____

☐ A   ☐ B   ☐ C   ☐ D   ☐ Register

_____

MY DECISION TODAY

☐ I'm committing my life to Christ.

☐ I want to be baptized.

☐ I'm renewing my commitment to Christ.

  Enroll me in the next ...

  ☐ Class 101: Introduction to Our Church Family.

  ☐ Class 201: Introduction to Spiritual Maturity.

  ☐ Class 301: Discovering My Shape for Ministry.

  ☐ Class 401: Discovering My Life Mission.

☐ I want to help at the church office.

☐ I want to help with children's programs.

I'M INTERESTED IN:

☐ Knowing how to commit my life to Christ.

☐ Growing in my relationship with Christ.

☐ Information on joining this church family.

☐ A small group: ☐ Couples ☐ Singles ☐ Men ☐ Women

Counseling: ☐ Pre-Marital ☐ Marriage ☐ Financial ☐ Personal

ACTIVITIES:

☐ Children	☐ Men	☐ Bible Studies
☐ Junior High	☐ Women	☐ Support Groups
☐ Senior High	☐ Seniors	☐ 12-Step Groups
☐ College Age(18–23)	☐ Parenting	☐ Business & Professionals
☐ Single Adults	☐ Single Parents	☐ Music
☐ Couples	☐ Child Dedication	☐ Recreation/Sport

COMMENTS, REQUESTS OR PRAYER NEEDS: ☐ For Prayer Team   ☐ Confidential

_____

_____

_____

SESSION 3 ~ ATTRACTING A CROWD TO WORSHIP

**This Business Reply Card is included with a
welcome letter to all first-time visitors.**

FIRST IMPRESSION CARD

Our church wants to serve you better. Would you give us your opinion please? Thanks!

This is what I noticed first:

_____
_____
_____

This is what I liked best:

_____
_____
_____

This is what I liked least:

_____
_____
_____

WORSHIP EVALUATION FORM
"Evaluate for Excellence"

Date: _____   Service Hour: _____

OUTSIDE:

Traffic Flow: _____

Parking: _____

Directional Signs: _____

Adequate Greeters: _____

Cleanliness of Bathrooms: _____

Cleanliness of Grounds: _____

Information Tables: _____

Refreshment Table: _____

Other Factors: _____

ALL STARS (Children's Sunday School):

Easy to Find: _____

Adequate Info Table Hosts? _____

Comments on All Stars: _____

Other Factors: _____

WORSHIP CENTER (Physical Appearance and Atmosphere):

Cleanliness: _____

Stage & Decorations: _____

Seating Arrangements: _____

Sound System: _____

Lighting: _____

Bulletins: _____

Ushers: _____

Other Factors: _____

SERVICE:

Comments on Service: _____

_____

Other Factors: _____

We are believers and belongers.

Session 4

Building Our Congregation

Turning Attenders Into Members

Now you are no longer strangers to God and foreigners
to heaven, but you are members of God's very own family
. . . and you belong in God's household with every
other Christian.

Ephesians 2:19 (TLB)

In Christ we who are many form one body, and each
member belongs to all the others.

Romans 12:5 (NIV)

People join what bring them meaning.

LEARNER'S GUIDE

Create a ___*climate*___ Where People Want to Join

The two things people crave most: (Love & Acceptance)

"By this all men will know that you are my disciples, if you love one another."

John 13:35 (NIV)

Accept one another, then, just as Christ accepted you, in order to bring praise to God.

Romans 15:7 (NIV)

FACT: GROWING CHURCHES LOVE, AND LOVING CHURCHES GROW!

Communicate that our church is a family, not an institution!

The glue that keeps them in is relationships

See the church as a family.

Communicate the _Value_ of Membership

The Three Parts of the Christian Life

1. Believing

    > **BELIEVE on the Lord Jesus and you will be saved.**
    >
    > **Acts 16:31** (TLB)

2. Belonging

    > **You are a member of God's very own family . . . and you BELONG in God's household with every other Christian!**
    >
    > **Ephesians 2:19** (TLB)

3. Becoming

    > **From the very beginning God decided that those who came to him . . . should BECOME like his Son . . .**
    >
    > **Romans 8:29** (TLB)

Benefits to Membership

- It identifies me as a genuine believer. Ephesians 2:19; Romans 12:5

- It provides me a spiritual family to support and encourage me. Galatians 6:1–2; Hebrews 10:24–25

- It gives me a place to discover and use my gifts in ministry. 1 Corinthians 12:4–27

- It places me under the spiritual protection of godly leaders. Hebrews 13:17; Acts 20:28–29

- It gives me the accountability I need to grow. Ephesians 5:21

Help people see "Membership" as a step of spiritual growth rather than as an organizational ritual.

SESSION 4 ~ BUILDING OUR CONGREGATION

Develop a _____*Plan*_____ to Assimilate New Members

Make plans by seeking advice.

Proverbs 20:18 (NIV)

QUESTIONS WE NEED TO SK

1. What does God expect from members of his church?

2. What do we expect from our members right now?

3. What kinds of people already make up our congregation?

4. How will that change in the next 5 to 10 years?

5. What do our members value?

6. What are new members' greatest needs?

7. What are our long-term members' greatest needs?

8. How can we make membership more meaningful?

9. How can we insure that members feel loved and cared for?

10. What do we owe our members?

11. What resources or services could we offer our members?

12. How could we add value to what we already offer?

Five Questions Prospective Members Ask

1. THE QUESTION OF ACCEPTANCE: DO I FIT HERE?

start affinity groups

2. THE QUESTION OF FRIENDSHIP: DOES ANYBODY <u>WANT TO</u> KNOW ME?

They are looking for friends.

3. THE QUESTION OF VALUE: <u>AM I NEEDED?</u> *?*

4. THE QUESTION OF BENEFIT: WHAT IS THE ADVANTAGE OF JOINING? *Biblical, practical benefits*

5. THE QUESTION O<u>F EXPECTATIONS:</u> WHAT IS REQUIRED OF MEMBERS?

SESSION 4 ~ BUILDING OUR CONGREGATION

Establish a Required _membership class_

**The manner in which people join our church will
determine their effectiveness as members for years to come.**

A strong membership class will grow a strong church.

OUTLINE OF CLASS 101:
DISCOVERING YOUR CHURCH FAMILY

SESSION 1: God's Purposes for Your Life

It is in Christ that we find out who we are and what we are living for . . . part of the overall purpose he is working out in everything and everyone.

Ephesians 1:11–12 (MSG)

Everything, absolutely everything, got started in him and finds its purpose in him.

Colossians 1:16 (MSG)

SESSION 2: Why You Need a Church Family

God's unchanging plan has always been to adopt us into his own family by bringing us to himself through Jesus Christ.

Ephesians 1:5 (NLT)

You are members of God's very own family . . . and you belong in God's household with every other Christian.

Ephesians 2:19 (TLB)

Love your spiritual family!

1 Peter 2:17 (MSG)

SESSION 4 ~ BUILDING OUR CONGREGATION

SESSION 3: Our Statements / What We Believe

> *Don't let others spoil your faith and joy with their philosophies, their wrong and shallow answers built on men's thoughts and ideas, instead of on what Christ has said.*
>
> **Colossians 2:8** (TLB)

> *Let there be real harmony so that there won't be splits in the church. Be of one mind, united in thought and purpose.*
>
> **1 Corinthians 1:10** (TLB)

4 STATEMENTS WE COVER IN OUR MEMBERSHIP CLASS

1. **Our Purpose Statement**
2. **Our Faith Statement**
3. **Our Lifestyle Statement**
4. **Our Circles of Commitment and Covenants**

SESSION 4: What It Means to Be a Member

> *Let the peace of heart that comes from Christ be always present in your hearts and lives, for this is your responsibility and privilege as members of his body.*
>
> **Colossians 3:15** (TLB)

- How God Wants His Church Organized

- The Two Ordinances of the Church: Baptism and Lord's Supper

- What It Means to Be a Member

- Our Membership Covenant

- What's My Next Step?

Develop a Membership _Covenant_

**The difference between "attenders" and
"members" can be summed up in one word:** _Commitment_

FACT: People will leave our church no matter what. When our church adopts a membership covenant, we are choosing who stays!

SESSION 4 ~ BUILDING OUR CONGREGATION

A PURPOSE DRIVEN MEMBERSHIP COVENANT

Having received Christ as my Lord and Savior and been baptized, and being in agreement with this church's statements, strategy, and structure, I now feel led by the Holy Spirit to unite with this church family. In doing so, I commit myself to God and to the other members to do the following:

1. **I Will Protect the Unity of My Church**

   - **By acting in love toward other members**
   - **By refusing to gossip**
   - **By following the leaders**

2. **I Will Share the Responsibility of My Church**

   - **By praying for its growth**
   - **By inviting the unchurched to attend**
   - **By warmly welcoming those who visit**

3. **I Will Serve the Ministry of My Church**

   - **By discovering my gifts and talents**
   - **By being equipped to serve by my pastors**
   - **By developing a servant's heart**

4. **I Will Support the Testimony of My Church**

   - **By attending faithfully**
   - **By living a godly life**
   - **By giving regularly**

Create Opportunities to Build _____

- Retreats
- Fellowship
- Name Tags
- Relational activities as a part of every meeting

Encourage Every Member to Join a _____

> *Let us consider how we may spur one another on toward love and good deeds. Let us not give up meeting together . . . but let us encourage one another . . .*
>
> Hebrews 10:24–25 (NIV)

Every _____ needs to be part of a small group!

SESSION 4 ~ BUILDING OUR CONGREGATION

Acts 2:42–47: Small Groups Are to Be Purpose Driven!

1. _____ *(Maturity)*

> *They devoted themselves to the apostles teaching . . .*
> > Acts 2:42a (NIV)

2. _____ *(Membership)*

> *And to the fellowship . . . and ate together with glad and sincere hearts . . .*
> > Acts 2:42b, 46b (NIV)

3. _____ *(Magnification)*

> *They devoted themselves to the breaking of bread and prayer . . .*
> > Acts 2:42b (NIV)

> *They were praising God . . .*
> > Acts 2:47a (NIV)

4. _____ *(Ministry)*

> *They gave to anyone as he had need . . .*
> > Acts 2:45b (NIV)

5. _____ *(Mission)*

> *And the Lord added to their number daily those who were being saved.*
> > Acts 2:47b (NIV)

Keep Communication Channels Open

Be sure you know the condition of your flocks; give attention to your herds.

Proverbs 27:23 (NIV)

People tend to be "down" on what they aren't "up" on!

Channels for Feedback

- The Welcome/Registration Card
- Email
- Small Group Leader Reports
- Prayer Chain
- Personal Calls and visits
- Social Media (Facebook, Twitter, etc.)

SESSION 4 ~ BUILDING OUR CONGREGATION

Channels We Can Use to Communicate a Message to the Congregation

- Social Media
- Online Directory
- Email
- Websites
- Video
- Voice mail
- Newsletters
- Prayer chains
- Mail
- Postcards

Make Our Members Feel Special!

Suggestions:

1. Print a nice certificate of baptism and membership

2. Take their picture!

3. New member banquets/receptions

4. Use public testimonies to create heroes in the church

5. Take their prayer requests seriously

6. Invite small groups to a Pastor's Coffee or Gathering

7. Staff Receptions

8. Send cards on special days

9. Give them a meaningful ministry role and freedom to do it

10. Challenge them with an eternal vision!

Personal Action Checklist

☐ **Do I welcome those who are new?**

☐ **Do I communicate the biblical value of membership?**

☐ **Have I attended the membership class? Do I encourage others to attend?**

☐ **Am I taking my covenant and commitment to other believers seriously?**

☐ **Do I take advantage of opportunities to build relationships?**

☐ **Am I part of a small group?**

☐ **Do I keep communication channels open?**

☐ **Do I make other members feel special?**

Let's also look at what we as a church could be doing better. Give our church a 1 (needs improvement) to 10 (doing well) in each of these areas. Which ones are we strongest in as a body? Where do we need some work?

__ **Create a climate where people want to join.**

__ **Communicate the value of membership.**

__ **Develop a plan to assimilate new members.**

__ **Establish a required membership class.**

__ **Develop a membership covenant.**

__ **Create opportunities to build relationships.**

__ **Encourage every member to join a small group.**

__ **Keep communication channels open.**

__ **Make our members feel special.**

Session 5

Developing Our Committed

Moving People from the Congregation into the Committed

XT is The model of perfect humanity

We are not meant to remain as children at the mercy of every chance wind of teaching . . . But we are meant to hold firmly to the truth in love, and to grow up in every way into Christ, the head.

Ephesians 4:14 (PH)

Brothers and sisters, because of the Lord Jesus we ask and encourage you to excel in living a God-pleasing life even more than you already do.

1 Thessalonians 4:1 (GWT)

Myths About Spiritual Growth

You can grow old w/o growing up.

Myth#1: Growth is automatic.

Myth #2: Growth is instant.

Myth #3: You can grow just by attending church.

Myth #4: You can attain maturity by yourself.

Myth #5: You measure spiritual growth by how much you know.

beliefs and behavior

How do you know when you have reached spiritual maturity?

> **You bear fruit!**

> *"Every good tree bears good fruit, but a bad tree bears bad fruit . . . By their fruit you will recognize them."*
>
> **Matthew 7:17, 20 (NIV)**

SESSION 5 ~ DEVELOPING OUR COMMITTED

The Purpose Driven Strategy Is Based On Eight Beliefs About Spiritual Growth

1. Spiritual Growth Is <u>intentional</u>

FACTS ABOUT COMMITMENT

- We become what <u>we are committed to</u> .

  Look more like Jesus

**A Great Commitment to the Great Commandment
and the Great Commission will not only produce a Great Church
but also a Great Christian!**

- Every Church <u>is known</u> by what it is committed to.

  *Among God's churches we boast about your perseverance and
  faith in all the persecutions and trials you are enduring.*

  2 Thessalonians 1:4 (NIV)

- You must <u>ask for commitment</u> or else you won't get it.

  If Jesus had to ask, we do too

- People want to be committed to something that _matters_, _has meaning_.

"Come, follow me," Jesus said, "and I will make you fishers of men."

                                            Matthew 4:19 (NIV)

2. *Spiritual Growth Is* _Incremental_

Knowing Christ, then Loving Christ, then Growing in Christ, then Serving Christ, then Sharing Christ.

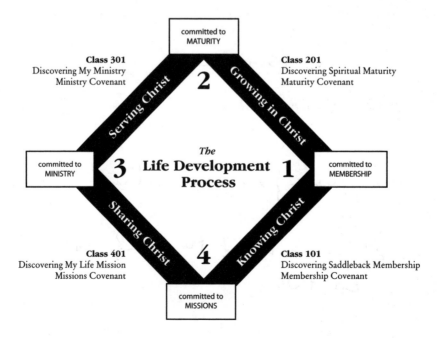

SESSION 5 ~ DEVELOPING OUR COMMITTED

When Jesus turned and saw [Andrew and John] following him, he asked, "What are you looking for?" They said, "Rabbi, where are you staying?" . . . He answered, "Come and see." So the two men went with Jesus and saw where he was staying and stayed there with him that day.

John 1:38–39 (NCV)

"If anyone would come after me, he must deny himself and take up his cross daily and follow me."

Luke 9:23 (NIV)

3. **Spiritual Growth Is** *Personal*

**We don't all grow spiritually the same way.
Some people learn best by listening. They grow through the ear-gate.
Others grow learn by reading. They grow through the eye-gate.
Some learn best by discussing. They grow through the mouth-gate.
Others learn by doing. They grow through the hand-gate.**

We grow the way θ wired us.

WHAT IS A SPIRITUAL GROWTH CAMPAIGN?

**An intensive, extended, all-church emphasis involving
every age group that focuses on a particular aspect of spiritual growth.**

- What On Earth Am I Here For?
- 40 Days of Community
- 40 Days of Love
- Life's Healing Choices
- 40 Days In the Word

God makes me responsible to do a personal evaluation of my growth.

> *Examine yourselves to see if your faith is genuine. Test
> yourselves. Surely you know that Jesus Christ is among
> you; if not, you have failed the test of genuine faith.*
> **2 Corinthians 13:5 (NLT)**

4. *Spiritual Growth Is* _____

> *"The second half of a man's life is determined
> by the habits he acquired during the first half."*
> **— Dostoyevsky**

> *Take the time and the trouble to keep yourself
> spiritually fit.*
> **1 Timothy 4:7 (PH)**

> **3 MOST IMPORTANT SPIRITUAL HABITS**
>
> **Putting Christ first in my Time, Money, and Relationships**
>
> 1. A DAILY _Time w/ ☉_
>
> Mark 1:35
>
> 2. A WEEKLY _tithe to ☉_
>
> 1 Corinthians 16:2
>
> 3. A COMMITTED _team for ☉._
>
> Hebrews 10:25

5. *Spiritual Growth Is* _Relational_

> *Let us be concerned for one another, to help one another*
> *to show love and to do good. Let us not give up the habit*
> *of meeting together, as some people are doing. Instead,*
> *let us encourage one another all the more.*
>
> **Hebrews 10:24–25 (TEV)**

You can't grow without being with people → love ☉ + love people.

THREE DECISIONS YOU CAN MAKE THAT WILL HELP YOU
GROW RELATIONALLY

*Dead Sea vs.
Sea of Galilee*

GET IN A SMALL GROUP
GET A SPIRITUAL COACH
BE A GROUP HOST OR SPIRITUAL COACH

6. *Spiritual Growth Is* *Multi-dimensional*

In Discipleship — We learn the truth of how God wants us to grow.
In Evangelism — We share God's truth.
In Ministry — We apply God's truth.
In Fellowship — We're held accountable for God's truth.
In Worship — We express appreciation for God's truth.

7. *Spiritual Growth Is* _____

8. *Spiritual Growth Is* _____

> *I have been crucified with Christ and I no longer live,*
> *but Christ lives in me. The life I live in the body, I live*
> *by the faith in the Son of God, who loved me and gave*
> *himself for me.*
>
> **Galatians 2:20** (NIV)

> *Christ himself carried our sins in his body to the cross,*
> *so that we might die to sin and live for righteousness.*
> *It is by his wounds that you have been healed.*
>
> **1 Peter 2:24** (TEV)

Personal Exercise

MY SPIRITUAL GROWTH PLAN!

☐ **SPIRITUAL GROWTH IS INTENTIONAL**

What specific commitment do I need to make to grow?

— Bible study (not just reading & listening) + prayer (⟹ faith)

☐ **SPIRITUAL GROWTH IS INCREMENTAL**

Do I have a long term plan for my growth?

— commitment to regular church attendance
— get in a home group
— keep meeting w/ Brad + Steve
— set annual goals

LEARNER'S GUIDE

☐ **SPIRITUAL GROWTH IS PERSONAL**

Do I learn better by listening, reading, discussing or doing? Am I involving myself in what best helps me to grow?

— yes; Works, semmonss, Scriptture
— The Brgo

☐ **SPIRITUAL GROWTH IS PRACTICAL**

What habits do I need to begin or renew for my growth?

See #1 — what are you calling me to? away from?

☐ **SPIRITUAL GROWTH IS MULTI-DIMENSIONAL**

Which of the five purposes do I need to work with God to strengthen?

SESSION 5 ~ DEVELOPING OUR COMMITTED

☐ **SPIRITUAL GROWTH IS SEASONAL**

Am I trusting God whatever the season of my heart or my circumstances?

☐ **SPIRITUAL GROWTH IS INCARNATIONAL**

Have I been trying to grow on my own power, or am I trusting more and more in Jesus' power?

Church Exercise

OUR SPIRITUAL GROWTH PLAN!

☐ **SPIRITUAL GROWTH IS INTENTIONAL**

What are the specific commitments we want to lead those in our church to make for their growth?

☐ **SPIRITUAL GROWTH IS INCREMENTAL**

How do we help people to start and continue in a plan for their growth? Do we need to start C.L.A.S.S.?

SESSION 5 ~ DEVELOPING OUR COMMITTED

☐ **SPIRITUAL GROWTH IS PERSONAL**

How could we better help people to learn by the different "gates" of listening, reading, discussing and doing? Do we need to have a campaign?

☐ **SPIRITUAL GROWTH IS PRACTICAL**

How do we encourage the habits of spiritual maturity? Is there one habit that we especially need to encourage right now?

☐ **SPIRITUAL GROWTH IS MULTI-DIMENSIONAL**

Which of the five purposes do we need to work with God to strengthen in our church?

LEARNER'S GUIDE

☐ **SPIRITUAL GROWTH IS SEASONAL**

Are there seasons that our members are facing right now in which we could give specific encouragement and direction for growth?

☐ **SPIRITUAL GROWTH IS INCARNATIONAL**

Is there something additional we could do to strengthen the message of trusting in Jesus' power and not our effort for our spiritual growth?

Session 6

Empowering Our Core for Ministry

How to Turn an Audience Into an Army

Gallup Survey

Only _____ of all laymen are active in a ministry.

An additional _____ **have no interest at all.**

BUT . . .

_____ **said they'd like to be involved
but have never been asked or don't know how.**

Teach the _____ for Volunteer Ministry.

4 Pillars of Volunteer Ministry: Romans 12:1–8

1. EVERY BELIEVER IS _____

2. EVERY MINISTRY IS _____

3. WE ARE DEPENDENT _____

4. MINISTRY IS THE EXPRESSION OF MY S.H.A.P.E.

SESSION 6 ~ EMPOWERING OUR CORE FOR MINISTRY

S _____ **(1 COR. 12; ROM. 12; EPH. 4):**

H _____ **(PROV. 4:23; PS. 37:4):**

A _____ **(EX. 31:3; 1 COR. 12:5):**

P _____ **(GAL. 6:4a MSG):**

E _____ **(ROM. 8:28; 2 COR. 1):**

Establish a Ministry Placement

STEP 1:
Attend "Discovering My Ministry" Class 301 and learn how God shaped you for ministry

Spiritual Gifts
Hearts
Abilities
Personality
Experience

STEP 2:
Complete your Personal S.H.A.P.E. Profile

STEP 3:
Commit to the Ministry Covenant

STEP 4:
Meet with a ministry guide for your S.H.A.P.E. interview and identify 3 or 4 possible ministries

STEP 5:
Meet with the staff who supervise the ministries you're considering

STEP 6:
Begin your ministry and start attending leadership training and support meetings

SESSION 6 ~ EMPOWERING OUR CORE FOR MINISTRY

Streamline Our Organizational Structure to Maximize Ministry and Minimize _____

The most valuable thing people give you is their time.

Provide _____ Training

Warning: Don't wear people out with pre-service training!

Never Start a Ministry Without a _____

The most critical factor in a new ministry start-up

is not the idea but the _____ .

Everything rises or falls on leadership!

Trust God's timing! Never force a ministry!

Establish Minimum _____

Don't bury them with procedures or committees.

Allow People to _____
Ministries Gracefully, without Guilt!

Give them freedom to do three things:

1. _____

2. _____

3. _____

SESSION 6 ~ EMPOWERING OUR CORE FOR MINISTRY

Provide the _____ **Needed**

1. Material Support: Keep Our Ministries Supplied!

Access to technology, space and materials.

2. Communications Support: Keep Our Ministries Informed!

**Develop multiple communication channels
to stay in touch with our core of lay leaders and ministers**

3. Promotional Support: Keep Our Ministries Visible!

- Set up ministry tables outside our building
- Give every minister a nametag
- Hold a ministry fair at least twice a year
- Print a brochure or set up a web page for each ministry
- Refer to ministries publicly from the pulpit
- Plan special events to honor our lay ministers

4. Moral Support: Keep Our Ministries Encouraged!

Delegate _____ **with Responsibility**

Trust people!

The Key to Motivation: _____

How to Bring Out the Best in Others

- Give them a _____
- Give them _____
- Give them the _____

People will be as creative as the structures allow them to be!

Always Keep _____ **Before Them**

The Nehemiah Principle:
Vision Must Be Renewed Every _____

SESSION 6 ~ EMPOWERING OUR CORE FOR MINISTRY

Personal Exercise

What do the four pillars of ministry say to you about your personal ministry?

4 PILLARS OF VOLUNTEER MINISTRY: Romans 12:1–8

    1. Every believer is a minister.

    2. Every ministry is important.

    3. We are dependent on each other.

    4. Ministry is the expression of my S.H.A.P.E.

Do they affirm what you are now doing, or cause you to think of a different ministry you might be doing?

Church Exercise

What do the 4 pillars of ministry say to you about the way our church helps its members to get involved in ministry?

4 PILLARS OF VOLUNTEER MINISTRY: Romans 12:1–8

    1. **Every believer is a minister.**

    2. **Every ministry is important.**

    3. **We are dependent on each other.**

    4. **Ministry is the expression of my S.H.A.P.E.**

How do you provide a clear path to ministry involvement for everyone?

How do you make sure that every ministry is valued?

How do you help people to discover their S.H.A.P.E. for ministry?

Session 7

Sending Our Commissioned

Reaching the World through The PEACE Plan

**Ordinary people
empowered by God
making a difference together
wherever we are.**

5 Global Giants: Our Greatest Problems

1. _____

2. _____

3. _____

4. _____

5. _____

SESSION 7 ~ SENDING OUR COMMISSIONED

The Church's Advantage — *We Have . . .*

1. *The Largest* _____

> *Through Christians like yourselves gathered in churches,*
> *this extraordinary plan of God is becoming known and*
> *talked about even among the angels!*
>
> **Ephesians 3:10** (MSG)

2. *The Widest* _____

> *All over the world this gospel is bearing fruit*
> *and growing . . .*
>
> **Colossians 1:6** (NIV)

3. *The Longest* _____

> *"I will build my church, and all the powers of hell will*
> *not conquer it."*
>
> **Matthew 16:18b** (NLT)

4. *The Fastest* _____

The believers rapidly multiplied . . .

Acts 6:1a (NLT)

The churches . . . <u>grew daily in numbers</u>.

Acts 16:5 (NIV)

5. *The Highest* _____

*"Love the Lord your God . . . and love your neighbor
as yourself."*

Matthew 22:37–39 (NLT)

6. *The Strongest* _____

*"<u>All authority</u> in heaven and on earth has been given to
me. Therefore go and <u>make disciples</u> of all nations . . .
And surely I am with you always . . . "*

Matthew 28:18–20 (NIV)

*With God's power working in us, God can do much, much
more than anything we can ask or imagine. To Him be
glory in the church . . .*

Ephesians 3:20–21 (NCV)

SESSION 7 ~ SENDING OUR COMMISSIONED

7. *The Simplest* _____

Each of you has been blessed with one of God's many wonderful gifts to be used in the service of others. So use your gift well.

1 Peter 4:10 (CEV)

8. *The Greatest* _____

"The Good News about God's kingdom will be preached in all the world, to every nation. Then the end will come."

Matthew 24:14 (NCV)

The Church's Antidote

PEACE

THE GLOBAL GIANTS

Spiritual Emptiness

Egocentric Leaders

Extreme Poverty

Pandemic Disease

Crippling Illiteracy

THE PEACE PLAN

Plant Churches

Equip Servant Leaders

Assist the Poor

Care for the Sick

Educate the next Generation

lant Churches

"I will build my church, and all the powers of hell will not conquer it."

Matthew 16:18b (NLT)

I always want to preach the Good News in places where people have never heard of Christ, because I do not want to build on the work someone else has already started.

Romans 15:20 (NCV)

The one who plants and the one who waters work together with the same purpose. And both will be rewarded for their own hard work.

1 Corinthians 3:8 (NLT)

Dear friend, when you extend hospitality to Christian brothers and sisters, even when they are strangers, you make the faith visible.

3 John 1:5 (MSG)

quip Servant Leaders

Pass on what you heard from me . . . to reliable leaders who are competent to teach others.

2 Timothy 2:2 (MSG)

"I have given you an example to follow. Do as I have done to you."

John 13:15 (NLT)

ssist the Poor

Pure and genuine religion in the sight of God the Father means caring for orphans and widows in their distress . . .

James 1:27 (NLT)

God blesses those who are kind to the poor. He helps them out of their troubles.

Psalm 41:1 (TLB)

When you help the poor you are lending to the Lord— and he pays wonderful interest on your loan!

Proverbs 19:17 (TLB)

are for the Sick

 ducate the next Generation

"Let the little children come to me, and do not hinder them, for the kingdom of heaven belongs to such as these."

Matthew 19:14 (NIV)

"The Spirit of the Lord is on me, because he has <u>anointed</u> me to preach <u>good news</u> to the <u>poor</u>. He has sent me to proclaim <u>freedom</u> for the <u>prisoners</u> and <u>recovery</u> of sight for the <u>blind</u>, to <u>release</u> the oppressed, to <u>proclaim the year of the Lord's favor.</u>"

Luke 4:18–19 (NIV)

Prayer

Jesus, I want to be an influence for good and for God. I ask you to make me a leader and use me anytime, anyway for your purposes. Help me to grow in maturity, to live with integrity, and to use my time and money with priority. I open my life completely to you. Come in and take over. In your name I pray. Amen

Personal & Church Exercise

Take a moment to think about what you and your church might be able to do to make a difference. Don't feel that you have to fill in all of the boxes below—just fill in the ones where a thought of what you or the church might do strikes you.

PERSONALLY . . .
is what you could do in your circle of relationships.

LOCALLY . . .
is what your church could do in your community.

GLOBALLY . . .
is what your church could do around the nation or the world.

LEARNER'S GUIDE

	PERSONAL	LOCAL	GLOBAL
Plant Churches			
Equip Servant Leaders			
Assist the Poor			
Care for the Sick			
Educate the Next Generation			

Appendix

Spiritual Health Assessment and
Spiritual Health Planner

Test yourselves to make sure you are solid in the faith.
Don't drift along taking everything for granted. Give
yourselves regular checkups . . . Test it out. If you fail
the test, do something about it.

2 Corinthians 13:5 (MSG)

Spiritual Health Assessment and Spiritual Health Planner

In Day 39 of *The Purpose Driven Life*, Rick Warren introduces the concept of a spiritual health assessment. He says that to maintain our physical health, we need regular check-ups with a doctor who can assess our vital signs—blood pressure, temperature, weight, and so on. For our spiritual health we need to regularly check and balance the five vital signs of a healthy Christian life:

WORSHIP: You were planned for God's pleasure.

FELLOWSHIP: You were formed for God's family.

DISCIPLESHIP: You were created to become like Christ.

MINISTRY: You were shaped for serving God.

EVANGELISM: You were made for a mission.

The Spiritual Health Assessment and Spiritual Health Planner measures your health at a particular point in time. It is not a tool to see how you measure up against other people; nor is it a tool to see how close you are to perfection. We all know we'll never be perfect this side of heaven. Rather, this is a tool that will help you evaluate your spiritual health, and give you direction for developing a plan to bring God's five purposes for your life into balance.

LEARNER'S GUIDE

How to Use this
Spiritual Health Assessment and
Spiritual Health Planner

This material is divided into the five purposes of Worship, Fellowship, Discipleship, Ministry, and Evangelism. To get the most out of this material we suggest you do the following:

1. Take the Spiritual Health Assessment

If you haven't already taken the *Spiritual Health Assessment* (on page 113), stop right now and take it. The assessment will give you a snapshot of your spiritual health, and pinpoint areas that may be out of balance. This will help you identify the purposes you would like to work on and those in which you are strong. We also highly recommend that you turn to the *Friend Feedback Assessment* on page 137 and ask a friend or spouse to fill it out for you. Just as with your physical health, it can often be helpful to get a second opinion.

2. Find the Purpose You Want to Work On

Find the purpose you would like to work on by transferring your assessment scores to the *Spiritual Health Plan* on page 138. We suggest you work on either the purpose with the lowest score on your *Spiritual Health Assessment*, or on a purpose the Holy Spirit may be nudging you to consider. When you have selected the purpose, locate the corresponding page in this *Spiritual Health Planner* for suggested steps and resources.

3. Choose a Crawl, Walk, or Run Step to Get Started

You will find a table for each purpose with a beginning step (crawl), an intermediate step (walk), and a more advanced step (run) for each of the questions found in the *Spiritual Health Assessment*. Pick the step or steps you want to take for the area you have chosen to work on. You will also find a resource page for each purpose with recommended books, small group studies, classes, and practical suggestions that will take you further in your growth.

4. Transfer the Steps to Your Spiritual Health Plan

Transfer the steps you have chosen to the *Spiritual Health Plan* on page 138.

5. Find a Spiritual Partner

Many of us start out with good intentions but lack the discipline to follow through with our plans. Make it a point to pair up with a spiritual partner who can help you follow through on the growth steps you have chosen to take. A Spiritual Partner is an individual, usually of the same gender, who is committed on an ongoing basis to helping you deal with life and all that it offers. This person should be a good friend who encourages you, helps with accountability when needed, and actively supports you as you take spiritual risks and face challenges unique to your life. One of your fellow small group members is likely to be this kind of friend.

LEARNER'S GUIDE

SPIRITUAL HEALTH ASSESSMENT

	doesn't describe		partially describes		generally describes

WORSHIP: You Were Planned for God's Pleasure

How I live my life shows that God is my highest priority	1	2	3	4	5
I am dependent on God for every aspect of my life	1	2	3	4	5
There is nothing in my life that I have not surrendered to (kept back from) God	1	2	3	4	5
I regularly meditate on God's Word and invite Him into my everyday activities	1	2	3	4	5
I have a deep desire to spend time in God's presence	1	2	3	4	5
I am the same person in public that I am in private	1	2	3	4	5
I have an overwhelming sense of God's awesomeness even when I do not feel His presence	1	2	3	4	5

Worship Total _____

FELLOWSHIP: You Were Formed for God's Family

I am genuinely open and honest about who I am	1	2	3	4	5
I regularly use my time and resources to care for the needs of others	1	2	3	4	5
I have a deep and meaningful connection with others in the church	1	2	3	4	5
I have an easy time receiving advice, encouragement, and correction from others	1	2	3	4	5
I gather regularly with a group of Christians for fellowship and accountability	1	2	3	4	5
There is nothing in my relationships that is currently unresolved	1	2	3	4	5
There is nothing in the way I talk or act concerning others that I would not be willing to share with them in person	1	2	3	4	5

Fellowship Total _____

DISCIPLESHIP: You Were Created to Become Like Christ

I am quick to confess anything in my character that does not look like Christ	1	2	3	4	5
A review of how I use my finances shows that I think more about God and others than I do about myself	1	2	3	4	5
I allow God's Word to guide my thoughts and change my actions	1	2	3	4	5
I am able to praise God during difficult times and see them as opportunities to grow	1	2	3	4	5
I find I am making better choices to do what is right when I am tempted to do wrong	1	2	3	4	5
I have found that prayer has changed how I view and interact with the world	1	2	3	4	5
I am consistent in pursuing habits that are helping me model my life after Jesus	1	2	3	4	5

Discipleship Total _____

MINISTRY: You Were Shaped for Serving God

I regularly use my time to serve God	1	2	3	4	5
I am currently serving God with the gifts and passions he has given me	1	2	3	4	5
I regularly reflect on how my life can have an impact for the Kingdom of God	1	2	3	4	5
I often think about ways to use my God-given gifts and abilities to please God	1	2	3	4	5
I enjoy meeting the needs of others without expecting anything in return	1	2	3	4	5
Those closest to me would say my life is a reflection of giving more than receiving	1	2	3	4	5
I see my painful experiences as opportunities to minister to others	1	2	3	4	5

Ministry Total _____

EVANGELISM: You Were Made for a Mission

I feel personal responsibility to share my faith with those who don't know Jesus	1	2	3	4	5
I look for opportunities to build relationships with those who don't know Jesus	1	2	3	4	5
I regularly pray for those who don't know Christ	1	2	3	4	5
I am confident in my ability to share my faith	1	2	3	4	5
My heart is full of passion to share the good news of the gospel with those who have never heard it	1	2	3	4	5
I find that my relationship with Jesus comes up frequently in my conversations with those who don't know him	1	2	3	4	5
I am open to going anywhere God calls me, in whatever capacity, to share my faith	1	2	3	4	5

Evangelism Total _____

Transfer your scores to the Spiritual Health Plan on page 138.

Spiritual Health Planner

Now that you have completed the *Spiritual Health Assessment* and transferred your scores to the *Spiritual Health Plan* on page 138, you are ready to take the next step toward living a healthy, balanced, purpose driven life.

Choose one purpose from the *Spiritual Health Plan* that you want to focus on. In the following pages you will find a table for each purpose with a beginning step (crawl), an intermediate step (walk), and a more advanced step (run) for each of the questions found in the *Spiritual Health Assessment*. Pick the step or steps you want to take for the area you have chosen to work on. You will also find a resource page for each purpose with recommended books, small group studies, classes, and practical suggestions that will take you further in your growth.

While you may need to challenge yourself to step up to the task, you also need to be realistic in your expectations, otherwise you might become discouraged and give up. So consider starting off with a crawl step—a target you can easily hit in the next thirty days. Then you can move on to a walk step—a tangible goal that will stretch you over the next sixty to ninety days. Finally, choose a run step—something that will require a leap of faith, but through the power of the Holy Spirit will bring you to a whole new level of spiritual maturity.

When you have selected the purpose you want to work on and the steps you want to take, we encourage you to share your decisions with a trusted friend who can help you stay the course by praying for you and holding you accountable. Don't try to do this alone. Isolation can lead to procrastination. But a loving friend can encourage you if you're feeling discouraged and help you up if you fall down.

Two are better than one, because they have a good return for their work: If one falls down, his friend can help him up. But pity the man who falls and has no one to help him up! Also, if two lie down together, they will keep warm. But how can one keep warm alone? Though one may be overpowered, two can defend themselves. A cord of three strands is not quickly broken.

Ecclesiastes 4:9–12 (NIV)

LEARNER'S GUIDE

WORSHIP

Using the chart below, choose a step you would like to take and transfer it to your *Spiritual Health Plan* page 138.

ASSESSMENT QUESTION	CRAWL	WALK	RUN
How I live my life shows that God is my highest priority.	Ask a friend or spouse to help you identify your top priorities. What changes do you need to make?	Spend time reading through the life stories of some of the people in the Old Testament. Journal about the characteristics in their lives that demonstrated that God was a priority. What principles could you implement in your own life?	Make it a daily habit to reflect on your activities for that day. Journal or spend time in prayer over how you saw God in your daily activities. How are your priorities shaped by a recognition of God's presence?
I am dependent on God for every aspect of my life.	Wake up with a prayer of thanks to God every morning.	Read through the Psalms. Note all the times the writer of the Psalms talks about his dependency on God. How do those words describe your own dependence on God?	Fast from food or some object on which you normally depend. Focus on God as you fast, and remind yourself how dependent you are on God for your life. Do this on a regular basis.
There is nothing in my life that I haven't surrendered (kept back) from God.	Take an inventory of your life and note everything you have not surrendered to God. Share your results with a friend. How can you work on these things to surrender them to God?	Set up a plan for giving up one thing you have held back from God. You may need to ask a friend or spouse to hold you accountable to do this.	Regularly fast from the things you have trouble surrendering to God. The "Suggestions" section on the next page lists several helpful tips for fasting.
I regularly meditate on God's Word and invite him into my everyday activities.	Meditate on a verse of Scripture on a daily basis. You may want to take some notes on what you have learned about God.	Set aside time to study God's Word on a daily basis. Pray and ask God for insight into his Word and how it can apply to your daily life.	Memorize Scripture. Choose some scriptures from your daily reading to memorize. Make it a priority to hide God's Word in your heart.
I have a deep desire to spend time in God's presence.	Give God a one minute prayer every day.	Set aside some time to go on a spiritual retreat to be alone with God.	Identify a place you can go to focus on God and worship him. Make it a habit to spend time in this place on a regular basis.
I am the same person in public that I am in private.	Have a friend or spouse complete the *Friend Feedback Assessment* found on page 137.0	Have a friend or spouse complete the *Friend Feedback Assessment* found on page 137.	Set up a regular appointment with a friend, spouse, or mentor to discuss how well you are living a life that is transparent. Allow this person to speak the truth to you, and to hold you accountable.
I have an overwhelming sense of God's awesomeness even when I do not feel his presence.	Study the names of God using the Psalms. You may want to keep a journal to remind yourself what you have learned about God.	Prepare yourself for a worship time using the method outlined in the "Suggestions" section on page 117.	Practice the presence of God in your everyday life. Use the methods in the "Suggestions" section on page 117.

Worship Resources

Books

The Purpose Driven Life: What On Earth Am I Here For? by Rick Warren (specifically Days 8 to 14)

The Way of a Worshiper by Buddy Owens

The Unquenchable Worshipper: Coming Back to the Heart of Worship by Matt Redman

The Air I Breathe: Worship As a Way of Life by Louie Giglio

Small Group Studies

(These resources are available at **www.SaddlebackResources.com**)

What On Earth Am I Here For? (6-week, video curriculum)

The Way of a Worshiper (4-week, video curriculum)

Doing Life Together: Surrendering Your Life for God's Pleasure (6-week, video curriculum)

Suggestions

PRACTICING THE PRESENCE OF GOD: Practicing the presence of God involves looking for God in every detail of life. To do this you may want to think of God as ever present in every situation, and remember you are never alone. Look at everything you do not as something you do by yourself, but something you do together with God. Spend time speaking with Jesus as if he were right there with you. Take some time to think about him every hour of the day.

FASTING: The purpose of a traditional fast is to abstain from food in order to focus clearly on your relationship with God. You can also fast from television, entertainment, reading, or anything that distracts you from God. Those who are diabetic, pregnant, or who suffer from severe physical disorders when fasting from food should fast from other things that are not physically damaging. Remember, the goal is to develop a focus on God. In order to fast you may want to consider the following:

- What is the purpose of this fast?

- Begin with something small like one meal or one time slot.

- During the fast, commit the time you would have spent eating to prayer, bible study, worship, etc. Use it as a time to focus on God.

JOURNALING: Sometimes it is helpful to journal in order to see God's work in our lives. You may want to start a journal that allows you to record some of the victories and struggles you are having. Record your thoughts and feelings as you go through a process of self-examination. Make it a point to review your journal annually to see how God has worked in your life over the past year.

WORSHIP: Find a place where you can worship God privately. It may be a spot outdoors, in the privacy of your bedroom, or even in your car while commuting to work with a good worship CD. Wherever it is, make a habit of visiting this place regularly and worshiping God there.

MEDITATE ON GOD: Take some time to meditate on who God is and to get a sense of his greatness. You may want to use the Psalms as a guide. Read through a Psalm and note what the psalmist says about God's character and about his experiences with God. Take some time to praise God for who he is and for what he has done in your life.

LEARNER'S GUIDE

WORSHIP AS A LIFESTYLE: Make it a point to see every action as a worship sacrifice to God. When you wake, thank him for the day. As you go to work or school, sing praise music or adore him for who he is. Throughout the day, try to commit every word, thought, and action to him as a way of thanking him and worshiping him, realizing every breath is his gift to us. At home, bring God into every activity. Talk with others about the things God has done in your life.

PREPARATION FOR CORPORATE WORSHIP: Spend some time preparing yourself for your church worship service. As you approach the building, take a moment to stop and thank God for your church. Before the service begins, say a prayer of thanks to God. Tell him you are looking forward to meeting him in worship. Pray that God would prepare your heart to worship him. Spend some time praying for the pastor and everyone involved in worship that day. Look around at those entering the church and pray for as many as you can specifically that God would touch their hearts and souls during the service. During worship, try to picture Christ seated on the throne (read Isaiah 6:1–8) and thank him for his sacrifice.

FELLOWSHIP

Using the chart below, choose a step you would like to take and transfer it to your *Spiritual Health Plan* on page 138.

ASSESSMENT QUESTION	CRAWL	WALK	RUN
I am genuinely open and honest with others about who I am.	Have a friend or spouse complete the *Friend Feedback Assessment* on page 137. Discuss openly the differences between how your friend/spouse views you and how you view yourself.	Honestly share your faults and struggles with someone who will commit to praying for you on a regular basis.	Give a testimony to your group or church about how God helped you in your struggles.
I regularly use my time and resources to care for the needs of others.	Pray for a need that someone has. Make it a point to ask them about it when you see them and pray for them on the spot.	Find someone who has a need in your small group or at church, and then meet that need.	Rally your small group to care for someone who has a need. Contact the church for more information on people who have needs in the church or community.
I have a deep and meaningful connection with others in the church.	Attend a worship service or class on a regular basis.	Take Class 101 or a similar church membership class, and become a member of your church.	Invite others to church.
I have an easy time receiving advice, encouragement, and correction from others.	Establish a friendship and share something of your life with that person.	Find a spiritual partner and meet with him or her about a specific issue in which you would like to grow.	Be a spiritual partner to someone else.
I gather regularly with a group of Christians for fellowship and accountability.	Attend a small group weekly.	Invite others to your small group.	Lead a small group weekly.
There is nothing in my relationships that is currently unresolved.	Pray for someone you have a conflict with. Make this a regular prayer that will move you towards reconciling the relationship.	Make it a point to seek forgiveness or give forgiveness to someone you have a conflict with.	Mend a broken or hurting relationship in your life, and seek to reconcile with that person.
There is nothing in the way I talk or act concerning others that I would not be willing to share with them in person.	Don't participate in gossip.	Challenge those who gossip to speak with the person directly.	Make it a point to share directly with a person instead of talking about the person behind his or her back.

Fellowship Resources

Books

The Purpose Driven Life: What On Earth Am I Here For? by Rick Warren
   (Specifically Days 15 to 21)

Relationship Principles of Jesus by Tom Holladay

Life Together: The Classic Exploration of Faith in Community
   by Dietrich Bonhoeffer

Small Groups with Purpose by Steve Gladen

Small Group Studies

(These resources are available at **www.SaddlebackResources.com**)

What On Earth Am I Here For? (6-week, church-wide campaign)

40 Days of Love (6-week, video curriculum)

Classes

Class 101: Introduction to Our Church Family (or a similar membership class
   at your church)

LEARNER'S GUIDE

Suggestions

SPIRITUAL PARTNERS: Search out a spiritual partner who will commit to meeting with you regularly and help you grow in your relationship with Jesus. It could be an older person or a peer. Set up a consistent time to meet together. It could be through email conversation or in person. This needs to be a person with whom you can openly share your struggles and ask for prayer, discuss behaviors you need to change and want to be held accountable for, share devotional insights you have learned in your personal study of Scriptures, and talk about general life issues.

ON-THE-SPOT PRAYER: Prayer is usually a great way to build community with others. The next time a person shares a need or concern with you, stop right there and ask if it is okay to pray for them. Make this a regular habit, and watch what it does for the level of intimacy you have with the people around you.

SEEK RECONCILIATION: For many of us, there are strains in our relationships that come from false perceptions or hurts we have chosen to harbor instead of heal. Take a look at your own life. Are there any strained relationships? Are you angry with someone else? Are you holding a grudge? Are you mad at God for not coming through for you? Are you always critical of yourself and others? As you reflect on your answers to these questions (there may be other questions you think of), make it a point to seek to be reconciled to people you are separated from because of these issues. You may want to talk with a counselor or your pastor before you seek reconciliation.

HOW DO YOU RELATE?: What relational problems are unmanageable for you? Are there patterns in your relationships that you repeat over and over again? What bad habits do you bring to your relationships? Many of us experience relational problems due to the ways we relate to others. Make it a point to explore these issues with a counselor, pastor, or spiritual partner.

LEARNER'S GUIDE

DISCIPLESHIP

Using the chart below, choose a step you would like to take and transfer it to your *Spiritual Health Plan* on page 138.

ASSESSMENT QUESTION	CRAWL	WALK	RUN
I am quick to confess anything in my character that does not look like Christ.	Evaluate your character.	Have a friend take the *Friend Feedback Assessment* found on page 137 and get feedback on the results.	Find a spiritual partner and establish a relationship of accountability.
A review of how I use my finances shows that I think more about God and others than I do about myself.	Give something to the church or someone in need.	Tithe the first 10% of your income to your church on a regular basis.	Give from your abundance above the first 10%.
I allow God's Word to guide my thoughts and change my actions.	Read one Bible verse a day.	Read the Bible straight through like a story or novel. See the "Suggestions" list on page 125 for more information on how to do this.	Make a regular habit of studying the Bible in depth. You may want to get some tools to help you or take a class at your church.
I am able to praise God during difficult times and see them as opportunities to grow.	During a crisis thank God for all he has done for you and how he will help you grow through this trial. Share what you are learning with a friend or mentor.	Journal about your circumstances to see how God is working in and through them. Spend some time reminding yourself of his work by re-reading what you have written.	Minister to others through the pain you have experienced by joining ministries at church that specifically focus on meeting the needs of those who are struggling where you have struggled.
I find I am making better choices to do what is right when I am tempted to do wrong.	Examine the areas of your life where you struggle with temptation. What are those areas of struggle and what should you start doing to avoid them?	Develop a plan for handling specific temptation in your life. Find a spiritual partner to help you.	Make confession and repentance a regular part of your time with God. Name the things you have done and commit yourself to making the right choices in the future.
I have found that prayer has changed how I view and interact with the world.	Pray a one sentence prayer from time to time to bring God into your circumstances.	Spend some time praying through structured prayers on a daily basis (see the "ACTS Model" or "The Lord's Prayer" in the "Suggestions" section on page 126).	Make spontaneous prayers a regular part of your day. (See "Flash Prayers" in the "Suggestions" section on page 127).
I am consistent in pursuing spiritual habits that are helping me model my life after Jesus.	Develop the spiritual habit of praying. After waking up, take a moment to offer a prayer to God.	Take Class 201 or a similar discipleship class at your church.	Commit to practicing regular spiritual habits on a daily basis such as quiet time, prayer, etc. Have a spiritual friend help you evaluate which habits you need to implement.

Discipleship Resources

Books

The Purpose Driven Life: What On Earth Am I Here For? by Rick Warren (Specifically Days 22 to 28)

Bible Study Methods by Rick Warren

The Way of a Worshiper by Buddy Owens

Knowing God by J. I. Packer

Attributes of God by Arthur W. Pink

Knowledge of the Holy by A. W. Tozer

The Life You've Always Wanted by John Ortberg

The Pursuit of God by A. W. Tozer

What's So Amazing About Grace? by Phillip Yancey

Small Group Studies

(These resources are available at **www.SaddlebackResources.com**)

What On Earth Am I Here For? (6-week, church-wide campaign)

Finding God in the Desert of the Soul (4-week, video curriculum)

40 Days In the Word by Rick Warren (6-week, video curriculum)

Foundations by Tom Holladay and Kay Warren (eleven, 4-week, video curriculum on the essential truths of the Christian faith)

1 Thessalonians 1: A Spiritual Road Map in a Mixed Up World (6-week, video curriculum)

1 Thessalonians 2: A Spiritual Road Map in a Mixed Up World (6-week, video curriculum)

James 1: Developing a Faith That Works (6-week, video curriculum)

James 2: Developing a Faith That Works (6-week, video curriculum)

Inside Out Living: Small Group Study on the Sermon on the Mount (6-week, video curriculum)

Managing Your Finances God's Way (7-week, video curriculum)

Classes

Class 201: Introduction to Spiritual Maturity (or a similar discipleship class at your church)

Crown Financial Ministries

Suggestions

BOOK STUDY: Choose a book of the Bible and commit to studying it in depth. Read through the entire book a few times. While doing this, get a basic understanding of how the book is structured, what the author's message is, who he is speaking to, what the book's purpose is, etc. Then start with a section of one chapter and read this through a few times asking the same questions as above. To help you in your study, you may want to pick up a commentary that helps explain things verse by verse.

LEARNER'S GUIDE

THE ACTS MODEL: The ACTS model of prayer involves breaking our prayers up into different phases or focuses. The "A" stands for adoration. The first portion of our prayers should focus on adoring God for who he is and giving him honor and glory. The "C" stands for confession. A very basic part of prayer is self-examination and coming clean before God about our sin, confessing it, and then turning from it. The "T" stands for thanksgiving. Thanksgiving involves thanking God for who he is and what he has done. The "S" stands for supplication, which involves bringing our requests before God. This model helps us stay balanced in our prayers and attuned to the will of God.

FASTING: The purpose of a traditional fast is to abstain from food in order to focus clearly on your relationship with God. You can also fast from television, entertainment, reading, or anything that distracts you from God. Those who are diabetic, pregnant, or who suffer from severe physical disorders when fasting from food should fast from other things that are not physically damaging. Remember, the goal is to develop a focus on God. In order to fast you may want to consider the following:

- What is the purpose of this fast?

- Begin with something small like one meal or one time slot.

- During the fast, commit the time you would have spent eating to prayer, Bible study, worship, etc. Use it as a time to focus on God.

JOURNALING: Sometimes it is helpful to journal in order to see God's work in our lives. You may want to start a journal that allows you to record some of the victories and struggles you are having. Record your thoughts and feelings as you go through a process of self-examination. Make it a point to review your journal annually to see how God has worked in your life over the past year.

THE LORD'S PRAYER: When asked by his disciples to teach them to pray, Jesus gave them what has come to be known as the Lord's Prayer. The Lord's Prayer is a model of prayer that can be broken up into six R's. The first three

LEARNER'S GUIDE

R's deal with prayers directed toward God. They are: Remember the Lord is near (*"Our Father in heaven"*—Matthew 6:9), Reflect on who God is (*"hallowed be your name"*—Matthew 6:9), and Refocus our lives toward his Kingdom and his will (*"your kingdom come, your will be done on earth as it is in heaven"*—Matthew 6:10). The second three R's deal with prayers for our needs. They are: Request the needs you have for today (*"Give us today our daily bread"*—Matthew 6:11), Repent of the sins you have committed (*"Forgive us our debts as we also have forgiven our debtors"*—Matthew 6:12), and Rest in God's deliverance and presence in times of temptation (*"And lead us not into temptation, but deliver us from the evil one"*—Matthew 6:13).

FLASH PRAYERS: Frank Laubach talked about "flashing" prayers at anyone you meet. He explained how he would pray silently for those he came into contact with and ask for God's joy and presence in their lives. He would "flash" these silent prayers at anyone he saw, people on the bus, the street, in a plane, etc. Take some time to experiment with this approach to prayer. At church you may want to flash prayers at those you pass by or see in the sanctuary. In every instance ask for God's joy and presence in the person's life. Then look for the response. Do you notice a difference in them?

THE BIBLE AS STORY: For many people Scripture can become dry because it is read like an encyclopedia. Take some time to read the Bible like a novel. Start at the beginning and read it straight through. Instead of looking for something to apply that day, look for overall themes and indications of what God is like and how he interacts with people.

MONEY MANAGEMENT: Take some time to look over how you manage your money. If you don't have a budget you may want to establish one. Spend some time praying over what God wants you to do with the money he has given you. This will then help you budget with God's priorities in mind. If you need help with this it may be a good idea to see a Christian financial counselor.

MINISTRY

Using the chart below, choose a step you would like to take and transfer it to your *Spiritual Health Plan* on page 138.

ASSESSMENT QUESTION	CRAWL	WALK	RUN
I regularly use my time to serve God.	See your family and/or job as a ministry.	Give one hour to serve at your church on a Sunday morning.	Commit to serve in a ministry at church that may require more time.
I am currently serving God with the gifts and passions he has given me.	Volunteer at your church.	Commit to serve in some kind of ministry.	Lead a ministry.
I regularly reflect on how my life can have an impact for the Kingdom of God.	List five ways your life can impact the Kingdom. Seek a pastor if you need help.	Take Class 301 or a similar ministry class at your church and discover your S.H.A.P.E. for ministry.	Commit to serve within a ministry that best expresses your S.H.A.P.E. for one year.
I often think about ways to use my God-given gifts and abilities to please God.	Take a spiritual gifts survey to discover your strengths.	Meet with your pastor to discover where your spiritual gifts and abilities can best be utilized in your church.	Start a new ministry in or through your church to serve others based on the gifts and abilities God has given you.
I enjoy meeting the needs of others without expecting anything in return.	Discuss with a friend five practical ways you can meet needs around you.	Pick one practical way to meet a need and do it.	Serve at the your church on a weekly basis helping out the staff.
Those closest to me would say my life is a reflection of giving more than receiving.	Serve at your church during the weekday helping out the staff.	Take on a volunteer project at your church.	Take on a leadership role within a ministry that best expresses your S.H.A.P.E..
I see my painful experiences as opportunities to minister to others.	Write out how Christ has healed or used a painful experience in your life for God's glory.	Share with a friend or your small group how Christ has healed or used this painful experience for God's glory.	Share this painful experience with your pastor to see if you can use it to help others in your church.

Ministry Resources

Books

The Purpose Driven Life: What On Earth Am I Here For? by Rick Warren
(Specifically Days 29 to 35)

The Call by Os Guinness

Improving Your Serve by Chuck Swindoll

S.H.A.P.E.: Finding and Fulfilling Your Unique Purpose for Life by Erik Rees

Small Group Studies

(These resources are available at **www.SaddlebackResources.com**)

40 Days of Purpose (6-week, church-wide campaign)

Doing Life Together: Developing Your Shape to Serve Others (6-week, video curriculum)

S.H.A.P.E. (6-week, video curriculum)

Classes

Class 301: Discovering Your S.H.A.P.E. for Ministry (or a similar ministry class at your church)

Suggestions

JOIN A MINISTRY: Join an existing ministry at your church that best fits your spiritual gifts, interests, passions, talents, abilities, personality type, and experiences.

JUMP IN ANYWHERE: You discover your gifts by getting involved in ministry. If you don't know your gifts and abilities yet, then just find something that sounds interesting and get involved. You'll never know what you're good at until you get started. If it doesn't work out, call it an "experiment" and try something else. *"If you wait for perfect conditions, you will never get anything done"* Ecclesiastes 11:4 (NLT).

START A NEW MINISTRY: You may have an idea for a ministry that does not currently exist at your church. Spend some time in prayer to determine if this ministry idea is something you would like to pursue. If it is, then contact your pastor or church leader who is in charge of ministries.

LEARNER'S GUIDE

EVANGELISM

Using the chart below, choose a step you would like to take and transfer it to your *Spiritual Health Plan* on page 138.

ASSESSMENT QUESTION	CRAWL	WALK	RUN
I feel personal responsibility to share my faith with those who don't know Jesus.	Take Class 401 or a similar evangelism class if it is offered by your church.	Lead your small group through an evangelism curriculum.	Lead a small group for seekers.
I look for opportunities to build relationships with people who don't know Jesus.	Invite an unsaved neighbor over for dinner.	Host a "Matthew Party" with your small group where you invite unsaved neighbors or friends over for dinner, a time of fellowship, or a social event.	Lead a seeker small group using "The Passion" curriculum.
I regularly pray for those who don't know Christ.	Identify names of unsaved people and pray daily for their salvation.	Ask your small group for names of unsaved friends and hold each other accountable to share your faith with them.	Do a prayer walk through your neighborhood, where you walk the block praying for each neighbor and any specific needs they may have.
I am confident in my ability to share my faith.	Write out your testimony and share it with a friend.	Lead your small group through a study focused on evangelism.	Volunteer for a local cross-cultural mission project.
My heart is full of passion to share the good news of the gospel with those who have never heard it.	Do a prayer walk through your neighborhood.	Lead a seeker small group using "The Passion" curriculum.	Volunteer for a local cross-cultural mission project.
I find that my relationship with Jesus comes up frequently in my conversations with those who don't know him.	Write out your testimony and share it with a friend.	Lead your small group through an evangelism curriculum.	Lead a seeker small group at work or in your neighborhood.
I am open to going anywhere God calls me, in whatever capacity, to share my faith.	Pray for an unsaved people group.	Volunteer for a local cross-cultural mission project.	Explore serving on a short-term mission trip.

Evangelism Resources

Books

The Purpose Driven Life: What On Earth Am I Here For? by Rick Warren
(Specifically Days 36 to 40)

Becoming a Contagious Christian by Mark Mittelberg and Lee Strobel

Say Yes to God: A Call to Courageous Surrender by Kay Warren

Small Group Studies

(These resources are available at **www.SaddlebackResources.com**)

40 Days of Purpose (6 week, church-wide campaign)

Wide Angle: Framing Your Worldview by Rick Warren and Chuck Colson
(6-week, video curriculum)

Doing Life Together: Sharing Your Life Mission Everyday (6-week,
video curriculum)

Dangerous Surrender: What Happens When You Say Yes to God
by Kay Warren (3-week, video curriculum)

Classes

Class 401: Discovering My Life Mission (or a similar evangelism class at
your church)

Suggestions

BE READY TO CARE: Be ready to care for the hungry or needy wherever you go. Carry gift certificates from your local grocery and department stores like Target® or Walmart® to give on the spot to those who have need, without worrying about cash. Carry the numbers for local shelters and food services with you so you can help the homeless. Buy an extra hamburger or bagel and share it with someone who needs it.

COMMUNITY COMPASSION: Look for opportunities to care for the needs of your community. There are many community programs that help share the love of Jesus through meeting the needs of others. Look for ways to take your faith outside the walls of your church.

DELIVER FOOD: Set aside some time to volunteer at your local food bank with your family or small group. Make it a special day or evening out. Allow everyone to participate in the food delivery process. Go out for a meal or dessert afterwards and talk about how it felt to serve others. How was Jesus seen through your actions?

WHAT'S YOUR STYLE: You may feel pressure when it comes to sharing Christ because you think you have to "sell" someone on Jesus. Sharing Christ can happen in many different ways. Take some time to explore your style. You could read *Becoming a Contagious Christian* by Lee Strobel and Mark Mittelberg, or attend a class at church. You may be more comfortable speaking directly to people about Jesus; or maybe it is easier for you to let it come up naturally in a conversation. Find your style and begin to share your faith with others.

SHORT-TERM MISSION: Choose to go on a short-term mission trip. Through these missions trips you get a better understanding of other people's need for Jesus, and a better understanding of the heart of God. Check out the short-term missions opportunities that are available at your church.

LEARNER'S GUIDE

COUNT CONVERSATIONS: Often we can put too much pressure on ourselves to "convert" someone or have all the right answers. It is the Holy Spirit who converts, not us. All you have to do is talk about the Gospel (*see* Matthew 28:19, 20). Instead of counting the number of people you have led to Christ, start counting the number of conversations you have with others about Jesus. You may be shocked to find how easy it is to talk naturally about Jesus when you don't pressure yourself to convert them.

PRAY FOR YOUR FRIENDS: Make it a point to pray specifically for people you know who don't know Jesus. You may want to write their names on a bookmark in your Bible, or in a prayer journal. Set aside a regular time in your day to pray for them.

Spiritual Health Assessment and Spiritual Health Planner

Friend Feedback Assessment Instructions

You have a rare privilege! You have been given this *Friend Feedback Assessment* by someone who trusts you. By asking you to fill it out on their behalf, they are telling you that your opinion matters to them. Most likely, you are a close friend, a spiritual partner, or a spouse who knows this person well, and they know you will respond honestly and prayerfully to this assessment.

Why are they taking the *Spiritual Health Assessment*? To maintain physical health, we need regular check-ups with a doctor who can assess our vital signs—blood pressure, temperature, weight, and so on. For our spiritual health, we need to regularly check and balance the five vital signs of a healthy Christian life:

WORSHIP: You were planned for God's pleasure.

FELLOWSHIP: You were formed for God's family.

DISCIPLESHIP: You were created to become like Christ.

MINISTRY: You were shaped for serving God.

EVANGELISM: You were made for a mission.

Your friend has already completed a self-assessment of their spiritual health. But just as with our physical health, it can often be helpful to get a second opinion. That's where you come in. Your role is really quite simple and should only take a few minutes of your time . . . but it could have a life-long impact on your friend. So here's what we are asking you to do.

LEARNER'S GUIDE

PRAY. Ask God to sharpen your mind and speak to your heart as you fill out the assessment.

Read each statement carefully, and respond to the best of your ability. If you can't answer a particular question because you don't know the person well enough, just give them a "3" for that question. You may want to mark those questions so your friend can identify them when you return the assessment.

Return the assessment to your friend and offer to answer any questions they might have.

Keep in mind that the *Spiritual Health Assessment and Spiritual Health Planner* measure our health at a particular point in time. It is not a tool to see how we measure up against other people; nor is it a tool to see how close we are to perfection. We all know we'll never be perfect this side of heaven. Rather, this is a tool that will help your friend evaluate their spiritual health, and give them direction for developing a plan to bring God's five purposes for their life into balance.

LEARNER'S GUIDE

FRIEND FEEDBACK ASSESSMENT

	doesn't describe		partially describes		generally describes

WORSHIP: You Were Planned for God's Pleasure

How I live my life shows that God is my highest priority	1	2	3	4	5
I am dependent on God for every aspect of my life	1	2	3	4	5
There is nothing in my life that I have not surrendered to (kept back from) God	1	2	3	4	5
I regularly meditate on God's Word and invite him into my everyday activities	1	2	3	4	5
I have a deep desire to spend time in God's presence	1	2	3	4	5
I am the same person in public that I am in private	1	2	3	4	5
I have an overwhelming sense of God's awesomeness even when I do not feel his presence	1	2	3	4	5

Worship Total _____

FELLOWSHIP: You Were Formed for God's Family

I am genuinely open and honest about who I am	1	2	3	4	5
I regularly use my time and resources to care for the needs of others	1	2	3	4	5
I have a deep and meaningful connection with others in the church	1	2	3	4	5
I have an easy time receiving advice, encouragement, and correction from others	1	2	3	4	5
I gather regularly with a group of Christians for fellowship and accountability	1	2	3	4	5
There is nothing in my relationships that is currently unresolved	1	2	3	4	5
There is nothing in the way I talk or act concerning others that I would not be willing to share with them in person	1	2	3	4	5

Fellowship Total _____

DISCIPLESHIP: You Were Created to Become Like Christ

I am quick to confess anything in my character that does not look like Christ	1	2	3	4	5
A review of how I use my finances shows that I think more about God and others than I do about myself	1	2	3	4	5
I allow God's Word to guide my thoughts and change my actions	1	2	3	4	5
I am able to praise God during difficult times and see them as opportunities to grow	1	2	3	4	5
I find I am making better choices to do what is right when I am tempted to do wrong	1	2	3	4	5
I have found that prayer has changed how I view and interact with the world	1	2	3	4	5
I am consistent in pursuing habits that are helping me model my life after Jesus	1	2	3	4	5

Discipleship Total _____

MINISTRY: You Were Shaped for Serving God

I regularly use my time to serve God	1	2	3	4	5
I am currently serving God with the gifts and passions he has given me	1	2	3	4	5
I regularly reflect on how my life can have an impact for the Kingdom of God	1	2	3	4	5
I often think about ways to use my God-given gifts and abilities to please God	1	2	3	4	5
I enjoy meeting the needs of others without expecting anything in return	1	2	3	4	5
Those closest to me would say my life is a reflection of giving more than receiving	1	2	3	4	5
I see my painful experiences as opportunities to minister to others	1	2	3	4	5

Ministry Total _____

EVANGELISM: You Were Made for a Mission

I feel personal responsibility to share my faith with those who don't know Jesus	1	2	3	4	5
I look for opportunities to build relationships with those who don't know Jesus	1	2	3	4	5
I regularly pray for those who don't know Christ	1	2	3	4	5
I am confident in my ability to share my faith	1	2	3	4	5
My heart is full of passion to share the good news of the gospel with those who have never heard it	1	2	3	4	5
I find that my relationship with Jesus comes up frequently in my conversations with those who don't know him	1	2	3	4	5
I am open to going anywhere God calls me, in whatever capacity, to share my faith	1	2	3	4	5

Evangelism Total _____

Transfer your scores to the Spiritual Health Plan on page 138 of this booklet.

LEARNER'S GUIDE

Spiritual Health Plan for _____

I will share my plan with _____ who will be my spiritual partner to help me balance the five biblical purposes in my life.

PURPOSES	PRACTICES	PARTNERSHIP	PROGRESS
What purposes are out of balance?	What do I need to do?	How will my spiritual partner help me in this purpose?	What progress have I made?
WORSHIP How I scored myself _____ How my friend scored me _____			
FELLOWSHIP How I scored myself _____ How my friend scored me _____			
DISCIPLESHIP How I scored myself _____ How my friend scored me _____			
MINISTRY How I scored myself _____ How my friend scored me _____			
EVANGELISM How I scored myself _____ How my friend scored me _____			

Additional Resources

For Purpose Driven Lives, Churches, and Pastors

Continue the Journey with Your Small Group!

We are constantly developing new and relevant curriculum specifically designed to deepen and strengthen the five purposes in your small group. We also have leadership tools and training materials to help small group leaders. Check us out at **www.SaddlebackResources.com**.

Learn More about Resources Available for Purpose Driven Lives at SaddlebackResources.com

Visit **www.SaddlebackResources.com** to learn more about resources that can support your journey toward living a purpose driven life. Register for free online daily devotionals, access Bible reading plans, and learn more about other offerings from Purpose Driven Life.

Learn More about Resources Available for Churches and Pastors at SaddlebackResources.com

Visit **www.SaddlebackResources.com** to learn more about *40 Days of Purpose*, *40 Days of Community*, and Purpose Driven conferences and regional events. You will find a wide variety of video-based small group curriculum to deepen the purposes in your congregation and community. You will also find practical insights and tools to help you apply the principles of *The Purpose Driven Church* to your church life. These principles have been implemented by pastors and church leaders of all denominations and sizes in America and around the world.

More Resources for Pastors Available at Pastors.com

Pastors may register online at **www.Pastors.com** to receive Rick Warren's weekly e-newsletter, *Rick Warren's Ministry Toolbox*. **Pastors.com** offers thousands of resources to assess, equip, and challenge both staff and congregation, as well as a comprehensive archive of sermons, articles, and key learnings geared to serve the unique needs of today's pastor.

_____

_____

_____

_____

_____

_____

_____

_____

_____

_____

_____

_____

_____

_____

_____

_____

_____

_____

_____

_____

_____

_____

_____

_____

_____

_____

_____

_____

_____

_____

_____

_____

_____

_____

_____

_____

_____

_____

_____

_____

_____

_____

_____